MME **CATASTROPHE**
à la fête foraine

MME **CATASTROPHE**
à la fête foraine

Roger Hargreaves

hachette
JEUNESSE

Ce jour-là, madame Catastrophe se rendit à la fête foraine.

Toi aussi, tu aimes bien les fêtes foraines, n'est-ce pas ? On y trouve toutes sortes d'attractions.

Madame Catastrophe visitait tous les stands. Qui sait ? Ses amis avaient peut-être besoin d'elle...

Elle s'arrêta chez monsieur Tatillon, le vendeur de barbe à papa, qui lui dit :

– J'ai un service à vous demander, madame Catastrophe. Pourriez-vous tenir mon stand un petit moment ? Figurez-vous que j'ai oublié de changer l'eau de mon poisson rouge.

– Ne vous inquiétez pas, je m'occupe de votre stand, répondit madame Catastrophe.

Justement arrivait madame Beauté. À l'occasion
de la fête foraine, elle était particulièrement en beauté.

– Bonjour, madame Catastrophe. Je voudrais une barbe
à papa assortie aux couleurs de mon chapeau.
Ra-vi-ssant, mon petit chapeau, n'est-ce pas ?

– Heu… oui !

Bzzzz !

Madame Catastrophe mit l'appareil à fabriquer
la barbe à papa en marche.

Et la barbe à papa monta, monta, monta, légère
comme un nuage de printemps !

Mais la barbe à papa déborda, et…

Madame Beauté se retrouva toute barbouillée
de barbe à papa.

Madame Catastrophe était bien embêtée et ne pouvait
que balbutier :

– Je… je suis désolée, vraiment désolée ! Et, confuse,
elle tourna les talons, laissant là la pauvre
madame Beauté, toute collante.

Ensuite, madame Catastrophe se dirigea vers le stand de tir.

Madame Catastrophe au stand de tir ! À ton avis, que va-t-elle bien pouvoir inventer comme nouvelle catastrophe ?

C'est alors qu'elle découvrit un étrange spectacle.

Monsieur Endormi, qui vendait des ballons, s'était endormi ! Monsieur Endormi s'envolait dans les cieux !

Il faisait peut-être de beaux rêves bleus…

Madame Catastrophe ne fit ni une ni deux.

Elle saisit une carabine, visa et…

Pan ! Pan ! Pan !

L'un après l'autre, les jolis ballons crevèrent
dans les cieux.
Envolés, les beaux rêves bleus !

Cette fois, monsieur Endormi était bien réveillé !

Il y eut un grand boum !

C'était monsieur Endormi qui venait de tomber
au beau milieu de la fête foraine, sous le regard
catastrophé de madame Catastrophe.

Elle avait voulu l'aider, et voilà ce qui était arrivé !

Pour se remettre de ses émotions, madame Catastrophe se dirigea vers le buffet. À l'occasion de la fête foraine, toutes les bonnes cuisinières de la ville avaient préparé de jolies salades.

– Allez me chercher des bols, madame Catastrophe ! ordonna madame Autoritaire. J'espère que, pour une fois, vous ne ferez pas de bêtises !

– Tout de suite, madame Autoritaire.

Le malheur, c'est que madame Catastrophe,
avec sa fâcheuse manie de frôler la catastrophe,
revint avec une pile de bols…

… mais une pile de bols géante !

Le sommet de la pile ne tarda pas à bouger, et même à tanguer dangereusement.

– Alors, ils arrivent, ces bols ? s'impatienta madame Autoritaire. Qu'est-ce que vous fabriquez ? On ne vous a pas demandé de danser un tango !

Madame Catastrophe tentait tant bien que mal de garder son équilibre… au prix d'incroyables acrobaties.

Un bol, deux bols, dix bols... Tous les bols dégringolaient. Madame Catastrophe s'agita de plus belle, essaya de les retenir et patatras !

La vaisselle se brisa en mille morceaux.

Qui s'agite ainsi, au beau milieu de la mayonnaise, de la sauce tomate et des salades ?

Madame Catastrophe, tu l'avais reconnue, n'est-ce pas !

– Hum ! Ah ! Je n'ai jamais goûté une salade de pommes de terre aussi délicieuse ! s'exclama madame Catastrophe.

Vous me donnerez la recette !

Tout le monde éclata de rire, même madame Autoritaire !
À ton avis, quelle a été l'attraction la plus appréciée de la fête foraine ?

Le numéro de madame Catastrophe et de sa pile de bols, bien entendu !

RÉUNIS VITE LA COLLECTION ENTIÈRE

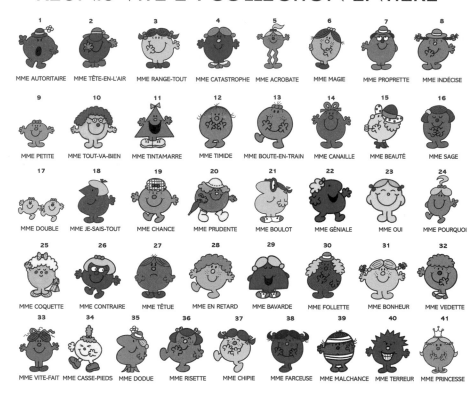

1 MME AUTORITAIRE
2 MME TÊTE-EN-L'AIR
3 MME RANGE-TOUT
4 MME CATASTROPHE
5 MME ACROBATE
6 MME MAGIE
7 MME PROPRETTE
8 MME INDÉCISE

9 MME PETITE
10 MME TOUT-VA-BIEN
11 MME TINTAMARRE
12 MME TIMIDE
13 MME BOUTE-EN-TRAIN
14 MME CANAILLE
15 MME BEAUTÉ
16 MME SAGE

17 MME DOUBLE
18 MME JE-SAIS-TOUT
19 MME CHANCE
20 MME PRUDENTE
21 MME BOULOT
22 MME GÉNIALE
23 MME OUI
24 MME POURQUOI

25 MME COQUETTE
26 MME CONTRAIRE
27 MME TÊTUE
28 MME EN RETARD
29 MME BAVARDE
30 MME FOLLETTE
31 MME BONHEUR
32 MME VEDETTE

33 MME VITE-FAIT
34 MME CASSE-PIEDS
35 MME DODUE
36 MME RISETTE
37 MME CHIPIE
38 MME FARCEUSE
39 MME MALCHANCE
40 MME TERREUR
41 MME PRINCESSE

DES **MONSIEUR MADAME**

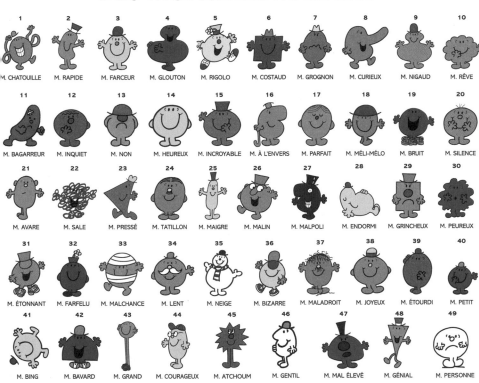

1 M. CHATOUILLE
2 M. RAPIDE
3 M. FARCEUR
4 M. GLOUTON
5 M. RIGOLO
6 M. COSTAUD
7 M. GROGNON
8 M. CURIEUX
9 M. NIGAUD
10 M. RÊVE

11 M. BAGARREUR
12 M. INQUIET
13 M. NON
14 M. HEUREUX
15 M. INCROYABLE
16 M. À L'ENVERS
17 M. PARFAIT
18 M. MÉLI-MÉLO
19 M. BRUIT
20 M. SILENCE

21 M. AVARE
22 M. SALE
23 M. PRESSÉ
24 M. TATILLON
25 M. MAIGRE
26 M. MALIN
27 M. MALPOLI
28 M. ENDORMI
29 M. GRINCHEUX
30 M. PEUREUX

31 M. ÉTONNANT
32 M. FARFELU
33 M. MALCHANCE
34 M. LENT
35 M. NEIGE
36 M. BIZARRE
37 M. MALADROIT
38 M. JOYEUX
39 M. ÉTOURDI
40 M. PETIT

41 M. BING
42 M. BAVARD
43 M. GRAND
44 M. COURAGEUX
45 M. ATCHOUM
46 M. GENTIL
47 M. MAL ÉLEVÉ
48 M. GÉNIAL
49 M. PERSONNE

Adaptation : Josette Gontier
Dépôt légal : mai 2011
ISBN : 978-2-01-224907-3
Loi n° 49-956 du 16 juillet 1949 sur les publications destinées à la jeunesse.
Imprimé et relié en France par I.M.E.

D02448

J136338

Gallery Books
Editor: Peter Fallon

THE MAI

Marina Carr

THE MAI

Gallery Books

The Mai
was first published
simultaneously in paperback
and in a clothbound edition
on 31 May 1995.
Reprinted 1997 and 2000.

The Gallery Press
Loughcrew
Oldcastle
County Meath
Ireland

© Marina Carr 1995

ISBN 1 85235 161 6

The Gallery Press acknowledges the financial assistance of An Chomhairle Ealaíon / The Arts Council, Ireland, and the Arts Council of Northern Ireland.

Characters

THE MAI, age 40
MILLIE, her daughter, age 16 and 30
GRANDMA FRAOCHLÁN, age 100
ROBERT, The Mai's husband, age 42
BECK, her sister, age 37
CONNIE, her sister, age 38
JULIE, her aunt, age 75
AGNES, her aunt, age 61

Time

Act One, Summer 1979
Act Two, one year later

The Mai was first produced in the Peacock Theatre, Dublin, on 5 October 1994, with the following cast:

MILLIE	Derbhle Crotty
THE MAI	Olwen Fouere
ROBERT	Owen Roe
CONNIE	Michele Forbes
GRANDMA FRAOCHLÁN	Joan O'Hara
BECK	Bríd Ní Neachtain
AGNES	Máire Hastings
JULIE	Stella McCusker
CELLIST	John O'Kane

Director	Brian Brady
Designer	Kathy Strachan
Lighting	Aedín Cosgrove
Design Co-ordinator	Karen Weavers
Music	Mícheál Ó Súilleabháin

for Dermot

ACT ONE

A room with a huge bay window. Sounds of swans and geese, off.
MILLIE *is standing at the window* (NOTE: MILLIE *remains onstage throughout the play.) Enter* ROBERT. *In one arm he has a travel bag, in the other a cello case. He looks around, examines the room in amazement, opens the double doors upstage, sees a music stand, turns aside thinking, and brings the bag and cello case into the room. He closes the door.*

THE MAI *passes the window, turns to look out on Owl Lake, hears a cello note, freezes — it stops — and decides she is dreaming. She enters the room, wearing a summer dress and carrying an armful of books. She places the books on the bookshelf, a few here, a few there. Drawn to the window, she looks out at the lake, waiting, watching. She places a few more books, then moves again to the window.*

A low cello note floats across the room. THE MAI *— startled — freezes, listens; the cello plays, melodic, romantic, beautiful.* THE MAI *moves to the double doors. She slides them across to reveal* ROBERT *engrossed in his playing. She listens, wanting to interrupt, yet also not. Now the piece finishes. Silence. For the first time* ROBERT *looks at her, cello bow in his hand.*

ROBERT Well — well — well.

> *He taps her shoulder, hip bone, ankle, on each of the 'Wells'.*

THE MAI Just look at you.
ROBERT You're as beautiful as ever.
THE MAI Am I?

> *Now he plays the cello bow across her breasts.* THE MAI *laughs.*

Softer.

11

ROBERT   Like this? Hmm?

THE MAI   Yeah.

ROBERT   (*He waves the bow around the room*) What's all this?

THE MAI   I built it.

ROBERT   All by yourself? How?

THE MAI   Just did.

ROBERT   And Owl Lake, my God, it's incredible.

THE MAI   You'll see it better in the morning.

ROBERT   In the morning. Will I? How did you know I'd come back?

THE MAI   Don't know — just knew.

> ROBERT *lifts* THE MAI *and carries her to a chair by the bay window, taking a bag from his belongings en route. He takes a scarf from the bag and ties it around her neck.*

It's lovely.

ROBERT   (*He produces perfume, tears the wrapper, and sprays it all over her*) It's the one you wear, isn't it, or have you changed?

THE MAI   It's the one I wear.

ROBERT   And these (*flowers*) are for you.

> *He produces a bottle of whiskey and a cigar.*

And this is for you (*whiskey*) and I'll have a shot as well.

> THE MAI *goes to the drinks cabinet, pours the whiskeys.* MILLIE *moves forward, looks at* ROBERT, *looks at* THE MAI.

Now let me see, is it Orla or Millie?

THE MAI   Millie.

ROBERT   Millie.

THE MAI   She's sixteen now.

ROBERT   I bought sweets for the children — but I suppose you're too big for sweets.

THE MAI   She's not too big for sweets yet.

ROBERT *places a box of sweets in* MILLIE*'s hands.*

MILLIE Where were you?
ROBERT Here — there —
MILLIE Everywhere. We were here all the time and in the old house.
ROBERT I know you were.
MILLIE Mom, will I get the others?
THE MAI Not yet, in a little while.
MILLIE Your jumper's lovely.
THE MAI You'd better hide it or she'll have it on her.
ROBERT (*He takes off the jumper*) Here, put it on. (*He puts it on her*)
THE MAI It's lovely on you — have a spray of perfume. And don't tell the others yet. I want it to be a surprise for them.

> ROBERT *and* THE MAI *exit hand in hand to the bedroom.* MILLIE *looks after them, moves around cleaning up, goes to the study, sounds a note on the cello, listens, looks out on Owl Lake.*

MILLIE When I was eleven The Mai sent me into the butcher's to buy a needle and thread. It was the day Robert left us. No explanations, no goodbyes, he just got into his car with his cello and drove away. So The Mai and I went into town and sat in the Bluebell Hotel where The Mai downed six Paddys and red and I had six lemon-and-limes. Then The Mai turned to me with her sunglasses on, though it was the middle of winter, she turned to me and said, Millie, would you ever run up to the butcher's and get me a needle and thread. Now at eleven I knew enough to know that needles and thread were bought in the drapery, but I thought maybe it was a special kind of thread The Mai wanted and because of the day that was in it I decided not to argue with her. So up I went to the butcher's and asked for a needle and a spool of thread and of course they didn't have any. Back I went to the Bluebell, sat beside The Mai and said rather gruffly, Mom, they don't sell needles and thread in the butcher's. Do they not, sweetheart? The Mai whispered and started to cry. Are you all right, Mom? I said. I'm grand, she said. Go up there and order me a Paddy and red. When I came back with the drinks The Mai said, Don't you worry about a thing, Millie, your Dad'll come back and we will have the best of lives.

Lights change. It's later that evening. Enter THE MAI *in a slip, wildly happy. She collects a bottle of whiskey off the cabinet and moves across to the window.*

THE MAI Look at the swans taking flight, Millie, aren't they beautiful?

And she drifts off.

MILLIE The Mai set about looking for that magic thread that would stitch us together again and she found it at Owl Lake, the most coveted site in the county. It was Sam Brady who sold the site to The Mai. For years he'd refused all offers, offers from hoteliers, publicans, restauranteers, rich industrialists, Yanks, and then he turned round and gave it to The Mai for a song. When asked by irate locals why he'd sold it to The Mai, a blow-in, Sam merely answered, *Highest Bidder!*

And so the new house was built and, once she had it the way she wanted, The Mai sat in front of this big window here, her chin moonward, a frown on her forehead, as if she were pulsing messages to some remote star which would ricochet and lance Robert wherever he was, her eyes closed tightly, her temples throbbing as her lips formed two words noiselessly. Come home — come home.

Light change. Daytime. The cello burst into song, wild, buoyant, practising. A huge currach oar moves across the window with a red flag on it. CONNIE *appears, stares in the window, nosey. She bangs the oar in her nosiness.*

GRANDMA F (*Off*) Would ya watch where ya're goin'!
CONNIE (*Shouts back*) Would you ever stop givin' orders from the car!
GRANDMA F (*Grumbling*) Shoulda carried ih meself!
CONNIE Ara dry up! Millie, how are you? Give us a hand with this, will you? Would it go through the window?

MILLIE *opens the window.*

THE MAI Ah you've arrived.
CONNIE Hello Mai.
THE MAI Easy, easy, mind the window.
GRANDMA F (*Off*) Mind me oar!
CONNIE God give me patience with that one! Nearly got us killed, her and her bloody oar.
THE MAI Leave it outside, we'll sort it out later.
CONNIE She'll nag us till it's in the bed beside her.
THE MAI Ara for God's sake, she's not sleepin' with it now!
CONNIE Don't even ask! How are ya, *a stóir*?
THE MAI Toppin', and yourself?
CONNIE The house is amazing, Mai, beautiful.

She hears the cello.

So he's here?
THE MAI Yeah, isn't it wonderful?
CONNIE Here, try it up this way.

GRANDMA FRAOCHLÁN *enters, leaning on* MILLIE.

GRANDMA F Show! Did ya do any damage ta ih?
CONNIE It's fine! Would you move out of the way or you'll be knocked down!
GRANDMA F Ah Mai, great ta see ya, *a chroí*.
THE MAI You've poor Connie moidered. (*She kisses* GRANDMA FRAOCHLÁN) Could we not put it in the garage?
GRANDMA F Well then ya can puh me in tha garage along wud ih.

15

CONNIE   That's the place for ya!

GRANDMA F   (*Nods towards the study*) An' whin did he arrive?

CONNIE   There! I have it! Millie, run round and catch it!

GRANDMA F   Aisy, aisy, go aisy an ih!

CONNIE   Would you ever! Honest ta God, you'd put years on me!

GRANDMA F   Sorry, *a stóir*, buh it's all I've left of him now. Why didn't ya build a bigger winda, Mai?

CONNIE   I've never seen one bigger! Ya needn't be turnin' on The Mai now! We had to saw through the banister to get it into our house.

GRANDMA F   Every time I move, ye have a hullabaloo abouh me oar!

CONNIE   Go in! Go in! Before I throw ya in the lake. We have it! We have it. (*The oar is finally in*)

GRANDMA F   Me bags, where are tha?

CONNIE   I've only two hands, Jesus!

THE MAI   How's Derek?

CONNIE   Askin' for you, the kids too.

GRANDMA F   I feel a bih wake, need a piece a chocolah. Connie, where's me chocolah?

CONNIE   Comin'! Comin'!

She goes off. THE MAI *leads* GRANDMA FRAOCHLÁN *in.*

GRANDMA F   Ya couldn'ta chose a nicer place, Mai, on'y —

THE MAI   Only what?

GRANDMA F   Well's noh tha sea, is ih? Why didn't ya move back ta Connemara like ya said ya would?

THE MAI   Ah I wouldn't get Principalship of another school so easy.

GRANDMA F   Ya'd be employed anawhere. Ya built this house for him, didn't ya?

THE MAI   And for myself and for the children.

GRANDMA F   Ya survived this long withouh him, why'a ya bringin' all this an ya'arself agin?

CONNIE *enters with bags.*

16

CONNIE There you go.
GRANDMA F Where's th'other bag?
CONNIE Millie must've brought it in.
GRANDMA F And me pinsion walleh, where's thah?
CONNIE How'd I know! Where'd you put it?
GRANDMA F Gev ih ta you.
CONNIE Did you? When — (*She looks in handbag*) — Oh, right, there you go.
GRANDMA F Chocolah.
CONNIE Which bag is it in?
GRANDMA F Can't amimber, look in all a thim.

CONNIE *glares at her.*

THE MAI Here. I have chocolate bought in for you.
GRANDMA F (*Taking the chocolate*) And where's tha hundert pound tha President gev me for me birta?

CONNIE *raises her hands in exasperation.*

Well, where is ih?
CONNIE (*Growls*) You spent it!
GRANDMA F Did I? Whin?
CONNIE Last week.
GRANDMA F On whah?
CONNIE On tobacco and pipes and chocolate and snuff and cigarettes and the Lord knows what!
GRANDMA F Thah's arrigh' so. Did I buy anathin' for you?
CONNIE No, you didn't.
GRANDMA F Very thoughtless a me, it's th'auld memory. Sorry, Connie.
CONNIE (*Lighting a cigarette, relieved the transfer is nearly over*) Ara I don't want anything.

THE MAI *and* CONNIE *exit.* CONNIE *beckons* THE MAI, *wants to see around the house.*

GRANDMA F Millie, a glass a mulberry wine there ta puh manners an tha ghosts.
MILLIE (*Gives her a glass*) Grandma Fraochlán?

GRANDMA F (*Dreamily, eating chocolate and drinking wine*) Hah, lovey?

MILLIE The name alone evokes a thousand memories in me. She was known as the Spanish beauty though she was born and bred on Inis Fraochlán, north of 'Bofin. She was the result of a brief tryst between an ageing island spinster and a Spanish or Moroccan sailor — no one is quite sure — who was never heard of or seen since the night of her conception. There were many stories about him as there are about those who appear briefly in our lives and change them forever. Whoever he was, he left Grandma Fraochlán his dark skin and a yearning for all that was exotic and un-attainable.

THE MAI *enters.*

GRANDMA F (*Looking around*) I don't know abouh all this, Mai.

THE MAI You're just like the rest of that Connemara click, always hoping that things will turn out for the worst! Well they won't! Because Robert is back and he's here for good and that's all I care about.

GRANDMA F I won't open me mouh agin!

THE MAI Ah now don't be like that. You know I'm delighted to have you here. Grandma Fraochlán, you don't realize how awful it's been these last few years, and now I have the chance of being happy again and I can't bear anyone to say anything that'll take that away.

GRANDMA F Ya shouldn't think like thah, Mai. Ya're strong, ya must be, look ah all ya done this last few years. Anaway, how is he?

THE MAI Never seen him more alive. You'd never think we were married seventeen years. I feel like a bride all over again.

GRANDMA F An' ya look like wan too. Ya're th'image a Ellen, God rest her.

THE MAI Am I?

CONNIE *enters.*

18

GRANDMA F More an' more every day. Ellen goh all tha brains an' all tha beauhy a my loh, just like you did ouha Ellen's loh.

CONNIE And I suppose Beck and myself are scarecrows.

GRANDMA F (*Ignoring her*) In me darkest hour I often wisht thah God had taken wan a th'others an' left me Ellen. Isn't thah an awful wish from tha mouth of a mother?

CONNIE You should be struck down.

GRANDMA F An' she was so proud a her three little girls — Mai, Connie an' Beck. Didn't she pick lovely names for ye ah a time in Connemara whin everywan was called Máire or Bridgín or Cáit. Oh she was way ahead a her time —

CONNIE Ah don't start.

GRANDMA F Won scholarships an' prizes inta tha best schools an' colleges i' tha country —

CONNIE We know! We know! (*Raconteur voice*) She was the only woman in her class doing Medicine the year she entered the Dublin university, and she did it all be herself, I had nothin' in those days —

GRANDMA F Shame on ya mockin' ya'ar own mother! And thin thah summer in Dublin, halfway through her college degree, an a wild nigh' a drink an' divilment, me darlin' girl goh pregnant be a brickie.

CONNIE Ara give over!

GRANDMA F (*Lost in memory*) Oh Lord, nineteen years a age, she had ta marry him, whah else could she do, ih was nineteen-thirty-eight.

A few mock tears from CONNIE.

Ya'd want ta show a bih more respect.

CONNIE I've run out of respect.

THE MAI We know all this, Grandma Fraochlán.

GRANDMA F Thin heed ih! Ya're too like her for my peace a mind!

CONNIE (*Listening to cello, looking around*) Well I don't know how you did it, Mai, it's a mansion — I mean Derek and I are on very good incomes and we'd never attempt something like this. Has he written anything worth talking about these last few years?

19

THE MAI He has. Loads.

CONNIE That's all very well but what're ye goin' to do for bread and butter.

THE MAI He's going back teaching in the college in the autumn.

CONNIE I thought he walked out of there after Julie's Michael gettin' him the job an' all.

THE MAI Well, he's sorted it out, they're delighted to have him.

GRANDMA F (Who has been dreaming and muttering to herself during the above exchanges) Would ya say I'll go ta heaven, Mai?

THE MAI Why wouldn't you, if there's such a place.

GRANDMA F If indeed, buh seriously now d'ya think I'm paradise material or am I wan a Lucifer's wicked auld childer?

THE MAI (Laughs) Paradise material definitely.

GRANDMA F I bin havin' woeful drames lately. I keep dramin' I'm in hell an' I'm tha on'y wan there apart from Satan himself —

CONNIE He'd be well matched.

GRANDMA F An' through a glass ceilin' I can see everywan I ever cared abouh, up beyant in heaven, an' d'ya know tha worst part a tha drame is Satan an' meself gets an like a house an fire. We're there laughin' an' skitterin' like two schoolgirls. Isn't thah a frigh'?

THE MAI Ara it's only a dream. Any word from Beck?

CONNIE She rang last week. Have you heard from her?

THE MAI Not in months.

CONNIE She's in great form, met a new man.

GRANDMA F Another wan.

CONNIE This time she said it's for real.

GRANDMA F Thah's whah she said tha last time an' tha time before. Whah does he do?

CONNIE I told you I didn't ask her.

GRANDMA F Well whah does his father do or did ya noh think a askin' thah aither?

THE MAI These things don't matter anymore.

GRANDMA F I remember tha first time I met tha nine-fingered fisherman. Is mise Tomás, scipéir, mac scipéara, he said. I knew where he was comin' from, wan sentence, wan glance a his blue eyes an' me heart was in his fist.

THE MAI Has she any plans to come home?

CONNIE You know Beck. Well I'd better be off.

THE MAI Have something to eat first. I've dinner made for you.

CONNIE I can't, Mai, I've a hundred and one things to do and Derek's expecting me, but thanks anyway.

GRANDMA F (*Who has been muttering to herself*) Buh ih doesn't mahher — I'm proud a Beck, proud a Connie an' proud a Tha Mai. Three great women! (*A bit tipsy, gets up to embrace them*)

THE MAI Sit down, *a stóir*.

GRANDMA F Mighy women tha loh a ye!

CONNIE She's off!

GRANDMA F If Ellen could see ye now! D'ya think she'd be happy wud tha way I rared ye? I'm so proud a ye! (*Swinging her glass, she spills the wine*)

THE MAI Mind the wine!

CONNIE Jesus, The Mai's new rug!

> GRANDMA FRAOCHLÁN *pays no heed, continues swinging the glass.*

Bye, *a stóir*.

> *She kisses* GRANDMA FRAOCHLÁN. *Exits.*

GRANDMA F (*In full flight, ignores* CONNIE's *exit*) An' I'm proud a Beck too, though she's flittin' from wan country ta tha next wud noh a stitch an her back nor a shillin' in her purse. Doesn't mahher. I'm proud. Mighy proud.

> THE MAI *and* CONNIE *drift off during this. We see* THE MAI *waving* CONNIE *off.*

MILLIE Grandma Fraochlán became a little sentimental after a few glasses of mulberry wine, and after a few more she began to call up the ghosts and would wrestle with them until sleep finally overtook her. These ghosts were as numerous as they were colourful. One of her favourite buddies from the ghost department was the Sultan of Spain.

21

GRANDMA F (*Incensed*) Now Sultan! You give me wan good reason why women can't own harems full a men whin ih is quihe obvious thah men owns harems full a women! G'wan! I'm listenin'! G'wan! Answer me thah! An' cuh ouh thah desert swagger! (*She listens earnestly, then with growing annoyance*) Seafóid Sultan! Nowhere in tha holy books does ih say thah! (*Listens*) I'll geh upseh if I want ta! G'wan! Off wud ya'arself! There's no gettin' through ta you! Don't know why I even waste me time wud ya! Off! An' God help tha harem thah has ta puh up wud ya!

MILLIE And she'd banish him back to his tent in the desert or to his palace in Morocco or his villa in Spain or to the exotic ghost section of her ancient and fantastical memory.

GRANDMA F (*Putting on lipstick*) Thah you, Tomás?

MILLIE A more intimate ghost was the nine-fingered fisherman, Grandma Fraochlán's beloved husband, who was drowned in a fishing accident some sixty years ago.

GRANDMA F (*Holds up lipstick*) Remember ya bough' ih for me — 1918 ah tha Cleggan fair — still have ih — Why wouldn't I? Remember tha Cleggan fair, me ninefingered fisherman, we wint across from Fraochlán in tha currach, me thirty-eighth birta, a glorious day — (*Listens, laughs softly*) I knew ya'd remember, ya'd goh me a boult a red cloth an' I'd made a dress an' a sash for me hair. Remember, Tomás, remember, an' ya toult me I was tha Queen a th'ocean an' thah natin' mahherd in tha wide worlt on'y me. An' we danced ah tha Cleggan fair an' ya whispert in me ear — sweet natin's — sweet natin's.

> GRANDMA FRAOCHLÁN *dances with the air; cello provides music, Irish with a flavour of Eastern. Let her dance a while. The music stops.* GRANDMA FRAOCHLÁN *stands there lost in memory.* ROBERT *enters.*

ROBERT You OK there, Grandma Fraochlán?

GRANDMA F (*Wiping off lipstick*) Grand, grand.

ROBERT Settling in all right?

GRANDMA F (*Sharply*) Are you?

ROBERT (*Smiles*) Yes, it's lovely here.

GRANDMA F (*Looking at him, the Mirada Fuerte*) I think ya on'y cem back because ya couldn't find anathin' behher elsewhere an' ya'll be gone as soon as ya think ya've found somethin' behher —

ROBERT You don't know the whole story and I'd advise you not to be —

GRANDMA F I know enough! Ya didn't see her strugglin' wud thim youngsters, all yours — in case ya've forgotten — scrimpin' an' scrapin' ta get this house built an' whin everythin's laid an, you appear an tha doorstep wud a bunch a flowers. Ah! (*Gesture of dismissal*)

ROBERT People change.

GRANDMA F I'm noh an this planeh wan hundert year withouh learnin' a thing or two. People don't change, Robert, tha don't change ah all!

ROBERT Well maybe if you and the rest of The Mai's family weren't livin' in our ear —

GRANDMA F I'm here as an invihed guest in Tha Mai's new house an' I'll lave whin Tha Mai axes me ta lave an' noh before!

ROBERT Grandma Fraochlán, I don't want to fight with you.

GRANDMA F Why couldn't ya a just lave her alone? Ya come back here an' fill tha girl's head wud all sourts a foolish hope. Ya'ar own father left ya'ar mother, didn't he?

ROBERT He never left her! He went to America for a few years. It was after the War, he had to get work, but he came back, didn't he!

GRANDMA F An' thousands sted, war or no war, or brung their wives an' childer wud em. Buh noh you, no, an' noh ya'ar father, an' sure as I'm sittin' here, ya'll noh be stoppin' long, because we can't help repeatin', Robert, we repeah an' we repeah, th'orchestration may be different but tha tune is allas tha same.

> ROBERT *exits.* GRANDMA FRAOCHLÁN *dozes. Light changes.* BECK *enters with a gift.*

BECK   Now you're not to tell anyone.
GRANDMA F   I won't, I won't, whah is ih?
BECK   The Mai'd kill me if she ever found out.

GRANDMA FRAOCHLÁN *opens the gift.*

Happy birthday, Grandma Fraochlán.
GRANDMA F   An opium pipe. Glory be, Beck, ya didn't!
BECK   Didn't I tell you I would.
GRANDMA F   I haven't seen wan a these in — in —
BECK   Is it the right kind?
GRANDMA F   Sure ih is. (*She takes a puff to test it*) There's greah pullin' in thah — Now did ya geh anathin' ta puh in ih?
BECK   Course I did. We'll have a wee smoke later on down in your room.
GRANDMA F   (*Still examining it*) Wud tha windas open, aye. We couldn't have wan now, could we?
BECK   (*A look around*) What ya think? (*A devilish smile from* GRANDMA FRAOCHLÁN) Come on.
GRANDMA F   Ya're th'original angel, Beck, th'original angel.

They exit. Evening. Lights up on THE MAI *and* ROBERT. *He plays a piece for her. She listens.*

ROBERT   (*Finishing*) Well?
THE MAI   It's very dark.
ROBERT   You're not crazy about it.
THE MAI   No, it's beautiful but —
ROBERT   But what?
THE MAI   I thought you'd write something lighter — happier — that's all.
ROBERT   Maybe next time I will.
THE MAI   Why'd you come back?
ROBERT   Why'd I come back? Difficult one — it's not so great out there, Mai.
THE MAI   Is it not?
ROBERT   No.
THE MAI   And I thought you came back for me.
ROBERT   I think maybe I did — you really want to know what

brought me back?

THE MAI   Yeah I do.

ROBERT   I dreamt that you were dead and my cello case was your coffin and a carriage drawn by two black swans takes you away from me over a dark expanse of water and I ran after this strange hearse shouting, Mai, Mai, and it seemed as if you could hear my voice on the moon, and I'm running, running, running over water, trees, mountains, though I've long lost sight of the carriage and of you — And I wake, pack my bags, take the next plane home.

THE MAI   So you've come back to bury me, that what you're sayin'?

ROBERT   Why do you always have to look for the bleakest meaning in everything?

THE MAI   It's usually the right one.

ROBERT   Not everything has to be final and tragic, Mai, not everything. And dreaming about death always means something else. Dreams aren't that vulgar, they're coy, elusive things. They have to be, the amount of times I've dreamt about you dying, and here you are healthy as a trout.

THE MAI   And just how many times have you dreamt of me dying?

ROBERT   I don't remember.

THE MAI   That many?

ROBERT   Don't tell me you haven't dreamt about me dying?

THE MAI   Once — only once — Was the night before we got married —

ROBERT   Yeah —

THE MAI   Remember Grandma Fraochlán had put you sleeping in the kitchen in front of the range?

ROBERT   Yeah —

THE MAI   And I was in the back room with Connie and Beck?

ROBERT   Yeah — And you crept out to me when the whole house was asleep.

THE MAI   Yeah — And we drank all Grandma Fraochlán's mulberry wine.

ROBERT   Yeah — And we had to whisper so we wouldn't wake the old crone.

25

THE MAI Yeah —

ROBERT (*Looking at her*) So, your dream.

THE MAI I dreamt it was the end of the world and before my eyes an old woman puts a knife through your heart and you die on the grey pavement, and for some reason I find this hilarious though I also know your loss will be terrible. Then the scene changes and I'm a child walking up a golden river and everything is bright and startling. At the bend in the river I see you coming towards me whistling through two leaves of grass — you're a child too — and as you come nearer I smile and wave, so happy to see you, and you pass me saying, Not yet, not yet, not for thousands and thousands of years. And I turn to look after you and you're gone and the river is gone and away in the distance I see a black cavern and I know it leads to nowhere and I start walking that way because I know I'll find you there.

ROBERT That's an awful fuckin' dream to tell anyone.

THE MAI Well, y'asked me to tell you.

ROBERT The night before we got married?

THE MAI Yeah — remember it like it was yesterday.

A pause. They look at one another. Hold a while.

ROBERT Mai, I've finished nothing this past five years — nothing I'm proud of.

THE MAI Have you not?

ROBERT I need you around me —

THE MAI So you came back for your work?

ROBERT No. Not only — All those years I was away, not a day went by I didn't think of you, not a day someone or something didn't remind me of you. When I'd sit down to play, I'd play for you, imagining you were there in the room with me.

THE MAI I used to talk to you all the time.

ROBERT I used to hear you.

THE MAI Used you?

He looks at her, plays her toes with his cello bow.

26

ROBERT Don't you know you are and were and always will be the only one? Don't you know, no matter what the hurtling years may do to us?

He hands her tickets.

THE MAI Tickets — For Paris — Both of us?
ROBERT And why not?
THE MAI I've never been to Paris.
ROBERT I know. C'mon, let's go into town for dinner.
MILLIE Can I go with ye?
ROBERT Ah? (*He defers to* THE MAI)
THE MAI Some other evening.
MILLIE Tch!
ROBERT Poor Millie's bored.
MILLIE Well I am! There's nothin' to do round here except chase tractors or listen to Grandma Fraochlán blatherin' about the nine-fingered fisherman.
ROBERT I'll take you in tomorrow for a surprise.

ROBERT *and* THE MAI *go out.*

MILLIE (*Watching them depart*) Maybe we did go into town the following day, I don't remember. It is beyond me now to imagine how we would've spent that day, where we would've gone, what we would've talked about, because when we meet now, which isn't often and always by chance, we shout and roar till we're exhausted or in tears or both, and then crawl away to lick our wounds already gathering venom for the next bout. We usually start with the high language. He'll fling the Fourth Commandment at me, *HONOUR THY FATHER!* And I'll hiss back, a father has to be honourable before he can be honoured, or some facetious rubbish like that. And we'll pace ourselves like professionals, all the way to the last round, to the language of the gutter, where he'll call me a fuckin' cunt and I'll call him an ignorant bollix! We're well matched, neither ever gives an inch, we can't, it's life and death as we see it. And that's why I cannot remember that excursion into town if it ever occurred. What I do remember, however, is one morning a year and a half later when Robert and I drove into town to buy a blue nightgown and a blue bedjacket for The Mai's waking. Still reeling from the terrible events of that weekend, we walked through The Midland drapery, the floorboards creaking, the other shoppers falling silent and turning away, they knew why we were there and what we'd come for, afraid to look yet needing to see, not wanting to move too closely lest they breathed in the damaged air of Owl Lake that hung about us like a wayward halo. No shroud for The Mai. It was her wish. In one of those throwaway conversations which only become significant with time, The Mai had said she wanted to be buried in blue. So here we were in a daze fingering sky blues, indigo blues, navy blues, lilac blues, night blues, finally settling on a watery blue silk affair. Business done, we moved down the aisle towards the door. A little boy, escaping his mother, ran from the side, banged off Robert and sent him backwards into a display stand. About him on the floor, packets of needles and spools of thread all the colours of the rainbow.

Daylight, sunshine, cello music, sound of children playing off. BECK *enters in swimming togs and a bathrobe, screeching and yelping from the lake.*
Enter THE MAI *with a boy's trousers, sewing them.*

BECK Well that's the end of my swimming for another summer. (*She pours a drink*) Will you have one?

THE MAI When I've finished this (*sewing*).

BECK (*Goes to window, waves at the children*) You're so lucky to have them all. I don't suppose I'll ever have a child now.

THE MAI You're still young enough.

BECK Mai, I'm thirty-seven.

THE MAI Wasn't St Elizabeth ninety-two when she had John the Baptist?

BECK You never take no for an answer, do you?

THE MAI And didn't the Duchess have Grandma Fraochlán when she was forty-five and didn't Aunt Julie have Barclay when she was forty-three?

BECK And didn't she make a right job of him! No, I won't have any now. I suppose there has to be one spinster in every generation.

THE MAI Honest to God, Beck, you'd swear you were on your last legs. Tell me more about this Wesley fella?

BECK Not much to tell.

THE MAI Don't be so cagey, you know I'm dyin' to hear.

BECK He's fifty-three and he thought I was thirty. He was married once before and he has two teenage sons who I got on better with than Wesley. I like being around young people, Mai — anyway Wesley was jealous, he was like a big baby sulkin' in the background but I didn't care. Brian, the older one, used to take me surfing and on my thirty-seventh birthday, thirty-first to them, he drove down from his college, a whole hundred miles, just to give me a birthday present. Of course Wesley couldn't handle this at all.

THE MAI Poor Wesley.

BECK Yeah — he wasn't really my sort, too educated for me, though I must say I've always been attracted to educated men, probably because of my own dismal academic record.

THE MAI You could've gone on and studied if you'd wanted.

BECK Not at all, I'm thick. Always was.

THE MAI You were never thick.

BECK Five *E*s in my Leaving Cert.

THE MAI Will you see him when you go back?

BECK Mai, I'm married to him.

THE MAI You're not!

BECK In a registry office five months ago, don't ask me why.

THE MAI Ah, why didn't you tell us?

BECK Because I'm getting a divorce.

THE MAI Ah you're not, Beck. Listen, congratulations anyway. (*Gets up to kiss her*)

BECK Ara would you stop! Now don't say a word to anyone.

29

The last thing I need is the Connemara click in on top of me.

THE MAI I won't open me mouth. Was it a lovely ceremony?

BECK It was, it was wonderful.

THE MAI I would've gone. Why didn't you invite me, Beck? Do you have any photos?

BECK I burnt them all.

THE MAI Ah you didn't, what happened?

BECK The only reason he married me was because he was afraid of getting old and being left alone.

THE MAI Is that what he said?

BECK No, of course that's not what he said. He made it seem like he was doing me a favour.

THE MAI Well it's not exactly Tristan and Isolde —

BECK Don't get me wrong, he was kind, kind enough until one night I got a little drunk and believed myself to be a lot closer to him than I actually was and I told him I wasn't thirty-one and that I wasn't in fact a qualified teacher but a low-down waitress.

THE MAI Ah, Beck, why did you have to tell him all those lies in the first place?

BECK Mai, you don't know what it's like out there when you're nothing and you have nothing, because you've always shone, always, you've always been somebody's favourite or somebody's star pupil or somebody's wife, or somebody's mother or somebody's teacher. Imagine a place where you are none of those things.

THE MAI It hasn't always been easy for me, Beck.

BECK You don't know what you're talking about.

THE MAI You didn't see me after Robert left me! What a struggle it was. You never wrote or phoned and Connie never came to see me, and yet the pair of ye kept in contact all the time, and now you sit in my new house and tell me I don't know what it's like.

BECK I never knew what to write, Mai. You know I'm useless in a crisis.

THE MAI You don't have to be. That's the easy option. You've an awful lot to offer anyone, if you'd just believe in yourself.

BECK The truth is, Mai, I've damn all to offer anyone. I can

30

THE MAI barely stay alive myself without getting involved in your hopeless affairs with Robert.

THE MAI He's my husband and he's back and I love him, so don't you freeway in here and tell me it's hopeless.

BECK Well it is, and Connie says so too.

THE MAI Well why doesn't she say it to my face? I never see Connie anymore. Anytime I suggest we meet she's busy. I'm fed up of it, Beck.

BECK Well that's between Connie and yourself, none of my business.

THE MAI Ye're thick as thieves, always were.

BECK You had Grandma Fraochlán, we had one another.

THE MAI That's no explanation. That's childhood. We had no choice then.

BECK And we've had none since! Wesley said I had the deportment of a serving girl — low voice, head down, don't interrupt anyone.

THE MAI It's a very cruel thing to say to anyone.

BECK Well it's the truth, isn't it!

THE MAI It's not how I would've described you or how anyone who cared for you would.

BECK Doesn't matter. It's over now anyway.

THE MAI You won't go back to him?

BECK I never give second chances, Mai. Don't believe in them. Anyway I knew it wouldn't last.

THE MAI Then why did you marry him?

BECK Ah I don't know.

THE MAI You don't know?

BECK (*Exploding*) I told you I was thick! I don't know! Maybe because everything I touch turns to shite! Now will you stop asking me all these questions!

THE MAI I'm sorry, Beck — I didn't mean to —

BECK Don't apologise! I'm the one who's sorry. I've no right to take it out on you. I'm just a bit under the weather these days. I'm thirty-seven years of age, Mai, and what've I got to show for it? Nothing. Absolutely nothing!

THE MAI You're still young, Beck. Why don't you do some kind of course here, get a job, settle down?

BECK I don't see the point, Mai. I can't think of any good

reasons to do anything ever again. (*Drinks*)

THE MAI *and* BECK *exit.*

MILLIE Needless to say, within days the story of Beck's liaison had travelled through the family like wildfire. None of The Mai's doing. No, Beck herself felt the need to tell everyone that she had been married, however briefly. I think maybe to raise herself a little in everyone's estimation.

> JULIE *and* AGNES *appear in fur coats, with similar handbags, outside the window, peering in, nosing around.*

AGNES (*Looking around furtively*) Well, what do you think?

JULIE A lot of money's been spent here. I wonder where they got it from.

AGNES Everythin's on credit these days. Would you look at the size of that window?

JULIE (*Peering in the window*) An ordinary house wouldn't do them. No, The Mai'd have to do the bigshot thing. I'd say they haven't two pennies to rub together. Is it my eyesight or is that a Persian rug?

AGNES (*Taking out glasses*) Show. It is. It is.

JULIE (*Taking glasses off* AGNES, *looking through them*) Not a mock one?

AGNES Show. (*Taking glasses back*) The genuine article.

JULIE They don't fall off the trees.

AGNES You can be sure of that, oh but isn't the view magnificent?

JULIE They could've bought a picture of a view.

> *They pass across the window.*

MILLIE Two of The Mai's aunts, bastions of the Connemara click, decided not to take the prospect of a divorcée in the family lying down. So they arrived one lovely autumn day armed with novenas, scapulars and leaflets on the horrors of premarital sex which they distributed amongst us children along with crisp twenty-pound notes. Births, marriages and deaths were their forte and by Christ, if they had anything to do with it, Beck would stay married even if it was to a tree.

JULIE *and* AGNES *enter, disarmed of their furs, but not their handbags which go everywhere with them.*

THE MAI (*Off*) Make ye'erselves at home, I'll be in in a minute.

AGNES Well that was lovely.

JULIE It was. I wonder how much the site cost.

AGNES What is it? Half an acre? You wouldn't get much change out of eight grand, not with a view like that.

JULIE Eight grand! Where did The Mai get hold of money like that with all those young ones?

AGNES They're a fine healthy clatter.

JULIE And she's manners on them. I'll say that for The Mai, she's a bit of *slacht* on that brood.

AGNES They've all plenty to say for themselves.

JULIE Maybe a bit too much to say, and the posh accents of them. Must be the schools she's sendin' them to. They didn't learn to speak like that around here.

AGNES That's for sure.

JULIE Still, they set to the washin' up and not a gig or a protest out a one of them.

AGNES And Robert there helpin' to serve up the dinner.

JULIE Thanks be to the Lord Jesus, though it might be just for show.

AGNES No, I was watching him, he knew where everything was and what needed to be done.

JULIE Thanks be to God he's back, one less to worry about. I wonder where he really was all that time.

AGNES Wasn't he in America?

JULIE You can be sure that's only the tip of the iceberg; strange crowd, tell you nothin'.

AGNES What'll we say to Beck?

JULIE We'll play it by ear. I wish to God she'd take that peroxide out of her hair.

AGNES She's a holy show in those tight black pants.

JULIE I hope to God she's not pregnant.

AGNES Glory be, I never thought of that.

JULIE (*Proud she's thought of it*) Oh you have to think of everything.

AGNES She'd never have it.

JULIE God forbid! A divorcée with a child, born after the divorce.

AGNES She'd never go for an (*Whisper*) abortion, would she?

JULIE We'll find out if she's pregnant first and, if she is, with the luck of God she'll miscarry.

AGNES Poor little Beck, she was always so nervous.

JULIE A jittery little thing from the outset, all that opium Ellen took and Grandma Fraochlán feedin' it to her.

AGNES It's up to us, Julie, to see that she's all right.

JULIE It is indeed. And isn't Grandma Fraochlán looking well?

AGNES She looks very stooped to me.

JULIE Not at all, she'll have to be shot. Here they are now. Go easy for a while, we'll have a bit of a chit-chat first. (*Cute wink to* AGNES)

AGNES (*Cute wink back*) I'll wait for you to start.

JULIE Grand. (*One more cute wink*)

> GRANDMA FRAOCHLÁN *enters on* BECK's *arm, followed by* THE MAI.

THE MAI Ye'll have a glass of sherry.

JULIE Not at all, we're grand.

> THE MAI *offers one to* AGNES. AGNES *looks at* JULIE *who is busy looking at* BECK's *belly.* AGNES *accepts.*

GRANDMA F (*Filling her pipe*) Still teetotallin', Julie?

JULIE When you give up the pipe I'll hit the bottle.

GRANDMA F You'll never drink this side a Paradise so. I'd hate ta die an' never've tasted sweet wine, wouldn't you, Beck?

JULIE You're looking great, Beck.

BECK I'm pushin' on, Aunt Julie.

AGNES None of us are spring chickens any longer.

34

JULIE (*To* GRANDMA FRAOCHLÁN) I see you're still on the mulberry wine.

GRANDMA F An' I'll be an ih as long as I can swalla.

JULIE You know it's against your doctor's orders. Mai, why're you letting her drink mulberrry wine?

THE MAI Ara it does her no harm and she enjoys it.

JULIE She wouldn't be allowed it in my house.

GRANDMA F Precisela why I never stay in your house, Julie, *a stóir*.

THE MAI Now Grandma Fraochlán, don't start a row. Remember you promised.

JULIE You were told no tobacco and no alcohol. I can't see why you can't obey two simple rules.

GRANDMA F Tha Lord puh grapes an' tabacca plants an th'earth so his people could get plastered ah every available opportunihy.

JULIE Ah there's no talkin' to you.

AGNES You're very quiet there, Beck.

THE MAI Have a whiskey, love, you're on your holidays.

AGNES Honestly, Mai, you get more and more like Ellen every day.

THE MAI Grandma Fraochlán's always sayin' that.

JULIE It's true and you've the same voice.

AGNES The very same. She'd be sixty now, a year younger than me.

JULIE It was shameful what happened to Ellen.

AGNES It couldn't be helped.

JULIE I'll never understand how a young woman in the whole of her health dies in childbirth in the best nursing home in Galway.

GRANDMA F She was worn ouh from all thim miscarriages and pregnancies.

JULIE Twenty-seven years of age. You should've looked after her better, Grandma Fraochlán.

GRANDMA F So ih was all my fault, was ih?

JULIE I'm not saying it was.

GRANDMA F Thin whah are ya sayin'?

JULIE Nothin', only I remember a few nights before she got married, she appeared on my doorstep, three months pregnant with The Mai there, and she begged me to take her in until the child was born and she wanted me to go and talk to you and make you see that she didn't have to marry him.

GRANDMA F An' why didn't ya!

JULIE If it was now I'd mow ya down!

GRANDMA F We're all wonderful after th'event, Julie, tha mebbe if we done this an' tha mebbe if we done thah! Why didn't ya come an' make me see an' why sih here an' tell me a lifetime too late?

JULIE Because I knew it would be pointless.

GRANDMA F Well thah's wan knife ya've buried in me an' ya're noh here two hours. Where's tha next wan?

AGNES (*Peacemaker*) What's Australia like, Beck?

BECK Oh it's beautiful.

AGNES Did you travel much around it?

BECK Yeah, I was all over.

AGNES And did you meet any aborigines?

BECK Several.

AGNES And what're they like?

BECK Well they're like ourselves, I suppose.

JULIE Indeed'n they are not! They live in caves, don't they, and they're black, black as ravens with teeth of snow. Sure didn't I see them on the telly!

BECK Most of them live in houses now. Only a few still live in caves.

AGNES And did you see the ones in the caves?

JULIE Wouldn't be my style at all!

BECK I did, I went on a camping holiday in the outback last summer.

JULIE (*Time for the jugular*) Was that where you met your husband?

BECK No, I met him in Sydney.

AGNES (*Dreamy*) In Sydney, Australia.

JULIE And when are we going to meet him?

GRANDMA F Ye're noh. Tha Mai toult y'all abouh ih an tha telephone.

AGNES You're not really getting a (*Whisper*) divorce, are you, sweetheart?

BECK I'm afraid I am.

AGNES Don't worry, don't worry.

JULIE None of ours ever got a divorce!

36

BECK   It just didn't work out, Aunt Julie. I tried. I really did.

JULIE   What's all this talk about working out. In my day you got married and whether it worked out or it didn't was by the way.

GRANDMA F   I didn't bring ya up ta think like thah, Julie!

JULIE   You didn't bring me up at all. I brought myself up and all the others. You were at the window pinin' for the nine-fingered fisherman!

THE MAI   Ah there's no need to be shoutin' now, Julie.

JULIE   Sorry, I'm only tryin' to help Beck.

AGNES   And what'll you do now, sweetheart?

JULIE   I don't like your carry on one bit, young lady! All this hoorin' around for years and finally someone marries you and you walk out on him. And I suppose you'll be back hoorin' around before we can bat an eyelid!

GRANDMA F   Ara, cop onta ya'arself, Julie! This is th'age a freedom, isn't thah righ', Beck?

JULIE   I still call it hoorin' around!

GRANDMA F   Mebbe a bih a hoorin' around would a done ya'arself no harm; might take thah self-righteous *straois* off ya'ar puss!

JULIE   You watch your dirty Arab tongue!

THE MAI   Go easy, the pair of ye!

GRANDMA F   I'm half Spanish, half Moroccan for ya'ar infor—

JULIE   Oh it's half Moroccan this time, is it! Last time it was three-quarters Tunisian!

GRANDMA F   I toult ya, y'eejit! Me greah grandfather was Tunisian! I'm on'y quarter Tunisian, half Moroccan an' half Spanish!

JULIE   That makes five quarters! How many quarters in a whole?

GRANDMA F   A good kick up yours is whah you need! Don't ya dare come tha schoolteacher wud me, ya little faggot ya!

THE MAI   Oh Jesus!

JULIE   No thanks to you I became a schoolteacher. If you had your way I'd still be out there on Fraochlán scrawbin' the seaweed off the rocks. Anyway it's all rubbish about the Tunisian and the Moroccan. You don't know where you came from!

AGNES This'll get us nowhere.

THE MAI Wouldn't ya think ye could be civil to one another at this stage of ye'er lives (*Points finger to* GRANDMA FRAOCHLÁN) And you promised you'd behave yourself.

GRANDMA F Sorry, Mai, sorry. It's a swanky auhum day, isna, Julie?

JULIE You haven't changed one bit, always fillin' our heads with stories and more stories —

AGNES Ah, Julie, leave it.

JULIE Whose side are you on?

AGNES I'm not on any side. And sure who knows but you'll marry a decent man yet, Beck. (*A glare from* JULIE) After the (*Whisper*) divorce, I mean.

BECK I think I'll end up like yourself, Aunt Agnes, without a man or a care in the world.

GRANDMA F Ya'll pilla a fine man yeh, Beck, don't mind ana a thim.

JULIE Are you still talking about sex at your age?

GRANDMA F Well I wasn't particularly, buh now thah ya mention ih, whah else is there ta talk abouh ah any age? Ya're born, y'ave sex, an' thin ya die. An' if ya're wan a thim lucky few whom tha gods has blesst, tha will send ta ya a lover wud whom ya will partake a thah most rare an' sublime love there is ta partake a an this wild an' lonely planeh. I have bin wan a them privileged few an' I know a no higher love in this worlt or tha next.

THE MAI You make our men seem like nothing.

GRANDMA F I on'y talk abouh me own.

JULIE Well maybe you should talk about him less, seeing as he left ya penniless with seven offspring.

GRANDMA F He didn't lave me. He was taken from me. He was given ta me an' he was taken from me, somethin' you would never understand, you who was seduced be ledgers an' balance sheets, installed in a house wud a slate roof an' an auhomobile be a walkin' cheque book who counted his thingamagigs as he cem —

JULIE You're a vicious auld witch!

THE MAI Grandma Fraochlán, that's enough! I mean it!

38

GRANDMA F Sorry, Mai, sorry, Julie, sorry, *a stóir*, it's me filthy foreign tongue. Julie, I calt y'after tha sunshine though ya were a child a winter, me on'y winter birth, me first born, greahest love abounding in ya'ar makin'. Mebbe parents as is lovers is noh parents ah all, noh enough love left over. Did we fail ya, *a stóir*?

JULIE You're the same, still the same, a dagger in one hand, a flower in the other — Well it doesn't wash with me anymore. (*Getting upset*)

THE MAI Ah come on now, Julie.

BECK (*To* GRANDMA FRAOCHLÁN) Come on, you and I'll go for a lie down.

JULIE Sorry, she provokes me.

GRANDMA F (*Being led away by* BECK *and* AGNES) Me pipe! I'm noh sittin' beyant in tha room 'till thah wan's gone, sans me pipe!

AGNES I have it, I have it.

GRANDMA F An' me mulberry wine.

AGNES Yes, yes.

GRANDMA F Ya blem me for everthin'! Y'allas have, an' y'allas will!

JULIE Ara whisht, Mom, or you'll drive me mad!

The three of them exit.

She takes it out of me everytime.

THE MAI Ah she's not the worst.

JULIE I'm sorry for fightin' in your new house, Mai —

THE MAI Ara for God's sake.

JULIE And don't hold it against me that I don't get on with her.

THE MAI Of course I won't.

JULIE A lot of things happened, Mai, long before you were born and I'm not just talkin' about Ellen.

THE MAI Julie, none of us are perfect.

JULIE I'm not talkin' about perfection. You didn't know her as a young woman. She was fiery, flighty. She had little or no time for her children except to tear strips off us when we got in her way. All her energy went into my father and he thought she was an angel. And

39

then when she was left with all of us and pregnant with Ellen, she was a madwoman. Mai, I'm not makin' it up. She spent one half of the day in the back room pullin' on an opium pipe, a relic from her unknown father, and the other half rantin' and ravin' at us or starin' out the window at the sea.

THE MAI Did she? She must've been heartbroken.

JULIE I know, I know. Several nights I dragged her from the cliffs, goin' to throw herself in, howlin' she couldn't live without the nine-fingered fisherman, opiumed up to the eyeballs. She was so unhappy, Mai, and she made our lives hell.

THE MAI It must have been terrible for you.

JULIE And then Ellen, she was brilliant, that girl was going places but there was something in Grandma Fraochlán that must stop it, and she did. She made that child marry that innocent. He wasn't Ellen's steam at all and he only married her because Grandma Fraochlán saw he did. He married her and then he left her on Fraochlán to rot. Came home every summer, left her with another pregnancy. And she belittled your father all the time to Ellen, till Ellen grew to hate him and looked down on him. He couldn't write or spell very well and Grandma Fraochlán would mock his letters until finally Ellen stopped writing to him. And at the same time she filled the girl's head with all sorts of impossible hope, always talkin' about the time she was in college, and how brilliant she was, and maybe in a few years she'd go back and study. And it only filled Ellen with more longing and made her feel that what she had lost was all the greater. And do you know the worst, the worst of it all, Ellen adored her and looked up to her and believed everything she said, and that's what killed her, not childbirth, no, her spirit was broken.

THE MAI Are you serious?

JULIE Well that's what I saw. Just be careful with Robert, don't let her interfere, she doesn't realise the influence she has over all of us. I'm seventy-five years of age, Mai, and I'm still not over my childhood. It's not fair they should teach us desperation so young or if they do they should never mention hope. Now where's my coat? Oh, I almost forgot, here's a little something. (*She produces an envelope from breast*)

THE MAI I wouldn't dream of taking it.

JULIE (*She puts it into* THE MAI's *dress, and produces another envelope from her other breast*) And that's for Beck. Don't let on I gave it to her. I can't be seen to be supportin' a divorcée.

THE MAI There's no sense to this —

JULIE He wasn't an aborigine, was he?

THE MAI Who?

JULIE Beck's husband?

THE MAI (*Controls a titter of amusement*) No — aah — he wasn't.

JULIE Not that I've anythin' against them. It's just these mixed marriages rarely work. There's plenty more (*Indicating envelope*) where that came from, so don't ever be stuck. I know you've had it rough.

JULIE *and* THE MAI *exit.*

MILLIE Owl Lake comes from the Irish, *loch cailleach oíche,* Lake of the Night Hag or Pool of the Dark Witch. The legend goes that Coillte, daughter of the mountain god, Bloom, fell in love with Bláth, Lord of all the flowers. So away she bounded like a young deer, across her father's mountain, down through Croc's Valley of Stone, over the dark witch's boglands till she came to Bláth's domain. There he lay, under an oak tree, playing his pipes, a crown of forget-me-nots in his ebony hair. And so they lived freely through the spring and summer, sleeping on beds of leaves and grass, drinking soups of nettle and rosehip, dressing in acorn and poppy. One evening approaching autumn Bláth told Coillte that soon he must go and live with the dark witch of the bog, that he would return in the spring, and the next morning he was gone. Coillte followed him and found him ensconced in the dark witch's lair. He would not speak to her, look at her, touch her, and heartbroken Coillte lay down outside the dark witch's lair and cried a lake of tears that stretched for miles around. One night, seizing a long awaited opportunity, the dark witch pushed Coillte into her lake of tears. When spring came round again Bláth was released from the dark witch's spell and he went in search of Coillte, only to be told that she had dissolved in a lake of tears. Sam Brady told me that when the geese are restless or the swans suddenly take flight, it's because they hear Bláth's pipes among the reeds, still playing for Coillte.

Ghostly light on the window. ROBERT *stands there with* THE MAI's *body in his arms, utterly still.* MILLIE *watches them a minute. Ghostly effect.*

A tremor runs through me when I recall the legend of Owl Lake. I knew that story as a child. So did The Mai and Robert. But we were unaffected by it and in our blindness moved along with it like sleepwalkers along a precipice and all around gods and mortals called out for us to change our course and, not listening, we walked on and on.

Lights down.

ACT TWO

The following summer.

Enter THE MAI *in a summer dress. She goes to the window, looks out, reaches into the pocket of her dress, takes the envelope with the card and ten-pound note out, looks at them hopelessly, and puts them back into her pocket.*

> BECK *and* GRANDMA FRAOCHLÁN *call, offstage.*

BECK Mai, how are you?

GRANDMA F Happy birta, Mai.

> THE MAI *waves at them from the window; they cross the window.*

THE MAI Ye had a good journey?

GRANDMA F I'm gettin' too auld for all this movin' abouh, Mai.

> *They pass into the house.*

THE MAI It's great to see you again, Grandma Fraochlán. (*Kisses her*)

GRANDMA F Ya'll be glad ta see tha back a me afore long.

THE MAI How's Connie?

BECK Askin' for you. Where's your gang? The house is very quiet.

THE MAI I sent them into the pictures. I wanted a bit of peace.

BECK And Robert?

THE MAI Gone away for the weekend.

GRANDMA F An' why didn't ya go wud him?

THE MAI Ah — the children — you know.

BECK I'd have stayed if you'd only asked.

THE MAI Ah it doesn't matter.

GRANDMA F Ih does. Why didn't ya tell us ya wanted ta go away?

BECK	No point in actin' the martyr.
GRANDMA F	I could as aisy as come up next weekend.
THE MAI	Ah will ye stop — it's pointless.

She starts to cry.

GRANDMA F	What's wrong, Mai?
BECK	Don't cry, sweetheart.
THE MAI	(*Pushing them off*) I'm all right, I'm all right, I'll be all right in a minute — I'm sorry about this — I didn't mean to spoil your —

Silence. GRANDMA FRAOCHLÁN *and* BECK *look at her in dismay.*

	(*Looking at them*) He gave me this (*birthday card*) and this (*ten-pound note*) and he's gone to Spiddal with her.
GRANDMA F	I knew this would happen.
THE MAI	(*Snaps*) Well then you knew more than I did.
BECK	Spiddal?
THE MAI	Yeah, where he used to take me.
GRANDMA F	An' who is she?
THE MAI	Everyone knows about it. It's been going on for months apparently. I should have known, I should have known.
GRANDMA F	An' whin did ya find all this ouh?
THE MAI	You know, he flew into a rage when I asked him, accused me of hounding him and spying on him and of course he denied it and I believed him — I was suspicious, of course, I am always suspicious of him, though I try not be be — And he was wining me and dining me, showering me with presents, telling me how much he loved me and then he'd be out till all hours, overly attentive to me when he was here. I must be blind — And then I followed him about two weeks ago and sure enough —
BECK	And who is she?
THE MAI	A local woman. I went into her office to talk to her — a cold brazen woman. If I was having an affair with

her husband and she came to see me, I think I would die with shame.

BECK Mai, you're too innocent. Half the country's having affairs with married men.

THE MAI Well, I could never do it. It's wrong and you can call me a prude if you like, and do you know what she said to me, she said that her relationship with Robert was none of my business. And she asked me to leave her office. I could have her out of this town pronto, if I wanted. Mike Clancy is an old friend, and if I asked him he'd transfer her.

BECK And why don't you?

THE MAI He's going to leave me again. I can't bear it a second time. Oh God, please, I can't bear it a second time.

BECK Here, Mai, sit down. Let me get you a drink.

THE MAI I know ye've been thinkin' all along that this was going to happen. Well I hope ye're happy now.

BECK Mai, we were hoping that it would all work out for you.

GRANDMA F We were indeed, *a stóir*.

BECK It'll all blow over in a couple of months, you'll see. If he's capable of loving anyone, it's you, Mai. Always has been.

THE MAI Love! If there was less talk about love in this house and more demonstration of it we might begin to learn the meaning of the word.

> GRANDMA FRAOCHLÁN *and* BECK *drift off during* MILLIE's *story.* THE MAI *sits at the window, smoking. Waiting for* ROBERT.

MILLIE The summer before Robert returned, The Mai found herself in London working as a sweeping girl in an Arab hairdressing salon. The banks would not give her a mortgage for the new house at Owl Lake unless her overdraft was respectable. The Mai figured if she lodged her teaching cheques and worked for the summer she'd be home and dry. We were sent to an old friend of hers, Cassie Molloy, a dressmaker with ten children of her own. What possessed The Mai to land the four of us on that poor woman is another story. What was certain was nothing was going to stop that house being built for Robert. We sat down to dinner in shifts and slept eight to a room while The Mai swept up the curls of Arab royalty. She told me the story of a little princess, already betrothed to some sheik or other, who came into the salon one day and fell for The Mai and insisted it was The Mai and only The Mai who washed and brushed her hair. The child began to come every day and before long they were playmates and The Mai's only job was to entertain the little princess who ran riot in the salon as long as she was permitted by her docile, shrouded mother who left magnificent tips. The Mai spoke longingly of this child, of how they played ring-a-ring-a-rosy, of the songs she taught her, of a shopping spree they went on together. A lick of jealousy would curl through me whenever The Mai mentioned her. I wanted to compete but I was out of my league and I knew it. But not The Mai, no, The Mai and the princess were two of a kind, moving towards one another across deserts and fairytales and years till they finally meet in a salon under Marble Arch and waltz around enthralled with one another and their childish impossible world. Two little princesses on the cusp of a dream, one five, the other forty.

> *It's evening, sound of a car door closing.* THE MAI *stands at the window.* ROBERT *walks past the window, and stops. He looks at* THE MAI. THE MAI *takes off her knickers, and throws them at him through the window! They land on his face.*

THE MAI (*Banging window*) Fuckin' bastard!

> ROBERT *stands there in shock. He passes into the house.* THE MAI *sits down, kind of smug, pleased with herself.* THE MAI *listens. We can hear* ROBERT *outside the door. He enters with the cello, the weekend bag*

46

*and the knickers. He stands there defiantly a minute:
nervous, guilty, at pains for some peace.* THE MAI
*looks him over, and looks away. He walks across the
room with the knickers, shakes them out, folds them,
and places them on the chair beside her.* THE MAI
watches their journey.

That all you can you can think of to do with them?
ROBERT What you expect me to do, eat them?

He leaves a bag on the chair beside her.

I brought you these.

He goes into the study, and sets up his cello.

THE MAI Strawberries and *Cosmopolitan* no less.

THE MAI *looks sarcastically at* ROBERT *who is half
watching her from the study.*

(*Reading the magazine*) The zipless fuck and how to
achieve it — How to take off seven pounds in seven
days — And here's a recipe for peach flan with
double cream. I suppose that's to put back on the
seven pounds you lost.

She flings the magazine on the chair.

ROBERT Grandma Fraochlán arrived all right?
THE MAI Robert, have you ever seen me reading *Cosmopolitan*?
Well, have you?

She eats some strawberries, a wan figure.

Did you buy them in Spiddal?
ROBERT No, why?
THE MAI They taste of the salt air.
ROBERT I bought them in Birr.
THE MAI They're lovely, have one?

She gets up, goes to the study, and proffers a straw-berry.

Go on.

ROBERT *goes to take it. She pulls it away.*

Here, let me feed you. Isn't that what lovers do?
ROBERT Mai, stop it.
THE MAI Come on.

ROBERT *moves away from her.* THE MAI *eats the strawberry. She moves around the study, sounds a note on the cello, takes the bow, begins screeching it across the cello to annoy* ROBERT.

ROBERT Look, will you leave it alone?

THE MAI *sits down and plays a few phrases expertly.*

THE MAI Not bad, hah? For someone who hasn't played in over fifteen years. With a bit of practice I'd be as good as you. Now there's a frightening thought — for both of us. How dare you throw ten pounds at me on my fortieth birthday!
ROBERT What you want me to do, take you to Spiddal and pretend everything is wonderful?
THE MAI Just because we're not in the first flush of passion doesn't mean we're pretending. And for your infor-mation I don't read *Cosmopolitan*!
ROBERT Fine.
THE MAI Do you know what I did this weekend, Robert, or do you care?
ROBERT Could you cut out the headmistress tone? You're not addressing Assembly now.
THE MAI I collected the children from their schools, I did twelve loads of laundry, I prepared eight meals, I dropped the children back to their schools, and I read Plato and Aristotle on education, because education is my business, and do you know the differences

between their philosophies? No, I didn't think you
would.

ROBERT It was I who brought Plato and Aristotle into this
house. When I met you, you were reading Mills and
Boons!

THE MAI You're a fuckin' liar! When you met me I was cellist in
the college orchestra! I had a B.A. under my belt and
I was half way through my Masters! You lower me, all
the time you lower me.

She brandishes the cello bow all over the place.

ROBERT Look, will you put that down, you'll break it.

THE MAI And so what, you'll replace it, you're good at replac-
ing things.

*She taps the bow along her toes, stops, pulls a string
from it, looks at* ROBERT, *looks away, resumes playing
herself: knees, thighs, stomach. Then she stops to snap
a string as it suits her. She plays her breasts and makes
notes on her throat with her other hand.*

(*Eyes closed, playing herself*) Tell me, Robert — Tell
me, is it that faraway pussies are greener or is it your
mother crowin' on your cock?

ROBERT You've a filthy tongue and the cut of a tinker.

THE MAI This is my house and I'll speak as I fuckin' well like!

ROBERT It's my house too. I gave you every penny I had for it
when I came back here — whatever possessed me.
Otherwise we'd have been out on the side of the
road. A fact you haven't bothered to mention to any
of your relatives! No! You'd rather have them all
thinking The Mai has done it singlehandedly again
in spite of that wayward bastard she married!

THE MAI So you want to reduce the conversation to money.
Right! Let's talk about money! Add this up! What it
costs to feed, clothe, educate four children for five
years. Do you know what that cost?

ROBERT No, I don't.

THE MAI Then keep your fuckin' mouth shut about your paltry little contribution. How can you do this to your children! They're haunted! Do you know that! Your children are haunted. And you don't give a fuckin' damn!

ROBERT I'm not listening to your fuckin' tirade and I refuse to take responsibility for the way you use the kids in our sham of a fuckin' marriage!

He exits slamming the door.
THE MAI sits there fuming. After a while she calms down and begins playing a few phrases until she gets them right. In full swing she finishes.

MILLIE Whatever about The Mai and Robert, Sam Brady had had enough. He'd always treated Robert with a quiet disdain, but now it was time for action. So one night he moved the fences in on either side of our house and we woke to find half the garden gone. He started throwing the ashes from his fire over our wall, a gesture considered a curse in that part of the country. He also figured a dose of Billy the Black was necessary. Billy the Black was his one obstreperous cow and she could always be depended on to do the damage. The farmers around were wary of Billy the Black. If you upset Sam, the next day you'd find your cornfield torn up by Billy the Black, and if you dared challenge Sam, well the next night your beet field would be in ribbons. Billy the Black was let loose in our garden, or what was left of it, and tore it to shreds. Sam Brady used to ride Billy like a horse. A bit of rope through her teeth, and he was off. If you happened to be walking up the strand at night and looked left across the churchyard field you would most probably see Sam galloping across the rise, bare-backed on Billy the Black, naked except for a pair of red bloomers it was said he stole from the King of the Tinkers' Bride. The whole neighbourhood revelled in nympholeptic glee at the outrageous passion of this mad bachelor, flying across the night on the flanks of his wicked cow. They called him the Rodeo Queen and, like myself, would come out to watch from a safe distance. Sam's final statement of his disapproval of Robert was to take his gun and blow the head off the cob feeding innocently near the bank. It's true what they say: swans do keen their mates. She circled him for days. The Mai was transfixed at the window. It's a high haunting sound that sings the once-living out of this world. It's a sound you hope never to hear again and it's a sound you know you will.

It's evening. THE MAI *comes on and pours a drink. Enter* CONNIE *and* BECK, *who have obviously been drinking.*

THE MAI (*To* CONNIE) So you finally came.

CONNIE The house looks beautiful, Mai, drivin' up the lane and the moon hangin' over it.

THE MAI (*Looks around*) This house — these days I think it's the kind of house you'd see in the corner of a dream — dark, formless, strangely inviting. It's the kind of house you build to keep out neuroses, stave off nightmares. But they come in anyway with the frost and the draughts and the air bubbles in the radiators. It's the kind of house you build when you've nowhere left to go.

BECK *and* CONNIE *stand there looking at her.*

Sit down for Christ's sake, pour ye'erselves a drink. (*To* CONNIE) So you've come to have a look?

CONNIE Do you want me to go, Mai?

THE MAI Of course I don't. Sit down, take it all in. Isn't it strange the fascination families have in the devastation of their nearest and dearest? I've noticed that.

BECK You're in a right mood tonight.

THE MAI Maybe they want to pick up a few tips for when their own number is up, or maybe it makes them feel good. They appreciate what they have themselves all the more. But really, Connie, you should have come last summer. Robert was just back, your children could've swam in Owl Lake — (*Whispers passionately*) It was a Jesus God of a summer!

CONNIE (*Softly*) We were away, Mai.

THE MAI You're always away, Connie.

CONNIE I don't have to explain my life to you, Mai. So you can leave out the big sister act. I'm my own person now and no one tells me what to do.

THE MAI I'm sorry, Connie. I'm delighted to see you. I miss you terribly. (*She kisses her*) How's Derek?

CONNIE He wanted to come here tonight to see you.

THE MAI Then where is he?

CONNIE Mai, he didn't want to meet Robert.

THE MAI He needn't have worried. Be easier get an audience with the Pope. Anyway it's great to see you again — reminds me of — the old days.

CONNIE Way back before we discovered men. You know I spent my twenties thinkin' I have to get a man, I have to get a man —

THE MAI So did I.

CONNIE Now that I have one, what's the big deal I'd like to know. Sometimes I'd love to be on my own again.

BECK Ara go on outa that. You wouldn't last a day. You've never been without a man as long as I can remember.

THE MAI Four engagements before Derek.

CONNIE And I never slept with any of them. If I could turn the clock back.

BECK Don't be ridiculous. Sex for the sake of it is just sex for the sake of it, like giving someone directions or telling someone the time.

THE MAI (*Innocently*) Is that what it's like, Beck?

BECK Well I think so, and ye needn't be looking at me now like I'm the Mata Hari.

THE MAI Have you slept with a lot of men, Beck?

BECK Put it this way, I've lost count.

CONNIE I'd like to try it out for myself, just once, go off to a hotel with someone I picked off the street or met in a pub or train, maybe a black man or an Arab — It's just I've never had a room to myself. I'd love a single bed of my own and then to head off to a hotel every now and then. Wouldn't that be just amazing? (*She sits back and laughs)*

THE MAI I think I might like that too.

BECK The pair of ye don't know how lucky ye are.

THE MAI Lucky.

BECK OK, Robert's playing puck at the moment but —

THE MAI That's putting it mildly.

CONNIE Is it that bad, Mai?

THE MAI I can't see a way out, not anymore.

CONNIE It's very simple, Mai. Just get up and walk, or kick him out. It was you built this house after all! No point in hangin' around to be knocked down again.

THE MAI You know the only difference between Robert and us is that Robert does what we dream about doing.

CONNIE Don't compare me with Robert.

THE MAI Robert goes to hotel rooms with this one and that one, like you said you'd like to do, Connie, but he always comes back to me. He always does and has done and always will.

CONNIE It's not much to be proud of, Mai.

THE MAI Think what you like.

CONNIE You're being very stubborn. You just won't admit to yourself how terrible all this is. Derek thinks it's absolutely dreadful the way he treats you.

THE MAI Well I don't like the way Derek treats Robert. All paly-waly for years and suddenly silence.

CONNIE Well if you want the truth, Derek won't come here because he has nothing to say to Robert, and he feels awkward with you. It's embarrassing, Mai, and I'm sorry, but an awful lot of people no longer speak to Robert. You'd want to hear what they're saying about him in town.

THE MAI You think I don't know that! But he's still my husband and I won't have you or anyone else say anything about him. I have the children to think of.

BECK Right, *a stóir*, we won't say another word.

THE MAI And you can tell your Mr Perfect, Derek, that he needn't be gettin' up on his high horse. Just because Robert isn't a model husband like himself. Everyone is deranged, Connie. Some manage to hide it better, that's all.

BECK Another one? (*She pours for herself*)

CONNIE And what's that supposed to mean?

THE MAI Don't be so harsh, Connie. Don't be so harsh and don't be so eager to write off other people's misery with glib observations and glib answers on a subject you know nothing about.

CONNIE I wasn't being glib, Mai, I'm only tryin' to —

THE MAI You don't know what it's like, the humiliation of it. The ground is gone from under me. I'm forty years of age, Connie, I'm on the downward slope.

CONNIE Indeed'n you are not.

THE MAI I am. Let's face facts. Another three, four years, the menopause, and what then?

CONNIE Life begins at forty, or so they say.

THE MAI That's crap from some women's magazine — probably *Cosmopolitan* — to boost the battered egos of haunted middle-aged women who know and feel their lives are falling down around their ears.

BECK C'mon, Mai, lighten up, we're celebratin'. Connie's here.

CONNIE You'll be all right, *a stóir*.

THE MAI For once in ye'er lives, will ye stop this family solidarity shite! You'll be all right *a stóir*! Well I won't be all right! I'll never be all right and neither will ye!

CONNIE Ara will you stop it. You're drunk!

THE MAI I'm not drunk! I'm trapped.

BECK You're tired, sweetheart, and a little drunk. It'll all look better tomorrow.

CONNIE I mean our lives are far from fairytales but, Christ, we're not dead yet!

THE MAI They sure are. Little did I think as I played around the cliffs of Fraochlán that I would ever be like this. I used to dream that a dark-haired prince would come across the waves on the wings of an albatross and he'd take me away to a beautiful land never seen or heard of before and he'd love me as no girl had ever been loved.

BECK My prince had a white horse.

CONNIE Mine had a chariot with golden bells that could sing my name.

THE MAI My God, we were some eejits.

BECK Too much listenin' to Grandma Fraochlán and her wild stories.

THE MAI She didn't prepare us at all.

CONNIE She did her best.

THE MAI She filled us with hope — too much hope maybe — in things to come. And her stories made us long for something extraordinary to happen in our lives. I wanted my life to be huge and heroic and pure as in the days of yore. I wanted to march through the world up and up, my prince at my side, and together we'd leave our mark on it.

CONNIE I suggest you look around for another prince, *a chroí*.

THE MAI Don't know any forty year old princes.

BECK Try for a king this time. You might have better luck.

THE MAI And I started off so well, gained entry everywhere I wanted, did exceedingly well academically, and I was good on the cello — I know I was — The more I think about it, the more I begin to realise that, one by one, I have to let go of all the beautiful things in my life, though I didn't mean to. Does everyone do that or is it just me?

BECK You're a hopeless romantic, Mai.

CONNIE (*A little jarred, begins singing softly*)
On the wings of the wind o'er the dark rolling deep
Angels are coming to watch o'er thy sleep,
Angels are coming to watch over thee,
So list' to the wind coming over the sea.

BECK (*While* CONNIE *is singing*) Remember we used to sing it in bed together?

THE MAI Should have stayed in that bed singing.

THE MAI *and* BECK *join in with* CONNIE.

ALL Hear the wind blow, love,
Hear the wind blow;
Lean your head over
And hear the wind blow.

ROBERT *enters unnoticed. He watches them, stares at*

THE MAI *as she begins singing, lost looking, in his*
overcoat, car keys dangling.

THE MAI (*Sings*) Daddy's a-sailing away out on the blue,
Sailing for herring of silvery hue,
Silver the herring and silver the sea,
And soon there'll be silver for baby and me.

ALL Hear the wind blow, love,
Hear the wind blow;
Lean your head over
And hear the wind blow.

MILLIE Joseph, my five year old son, has never been to Owl
Lake. I thought of having him adopted but would not
part with him when the time came, and I'm glad,
though I know it's hard for him. Already he is watch-
ful and expects far too little of me, something I must
have taught him unknown to myself. He is begin-
ning to get curious about his father and I don't know
what to tell him. I tell him all the good things. I say
your Daddy is an El Salvadorian drummer who
swept me off my feet when I was lost in New York. I
tell him his eyes are brown and his hair is black and
that he loved to drink Jack Daniels by the neck. I tell
him that high on hash or marijuana or god-knows-
what we danced on the roof of a tenement building in
Brooklyn to one of Robert's cello recordings.

I do not tell him that he is married with two sons to
a jaded uptown society girl or that I tricked him into
conceiving you because I thought it possible to have
something for myself that didn't stink of Owl Lake. I
do not tell him that on the day you were born, this
jaded society queen sauntered into the hospital,
chucked you under the chin, told me I was your
Daddy's last walk on the wild side, gave me a cheque
for five thousand dollars and said, you're on your
own now, kiddo. And she was right. I had no
business streelin' into her life, however tired it was.
I do not tell him that, when you were two, I wrote a
sensible letter, enclosing a photograph of you, asking
him to acknowledge paternity. And I do not tell him

he didn't answer.

THE MAI *enters in a stunning black ballgown.*

THE MAI Will you zip me up, Millie?

BECK (*With a pair of shoes*) These the ones you mean?

THE MAI Yeah. (*She does a twirl*) What do you think?

BECK Beautiful.

MILLIE You look gorgeous, Mom.

GRANDMA F (*Entering*) Oh ya're fierce swanky tanigh', Mai.

THE MAI Are you sure? I want to look my best. We're the guests of honour, you know.

GRANDMA F Ya'll be tha quane a thim all.

THE MAI (*Examining herself, back and front*) Really, do you think?

GRANDMA F Ya're stunnin' an' ya know ya're.

BECK Relax, Mai, it's only a dress dance.

THE MAI (*Flustered*) It's not! It's the Lion's Ball, it's a huge affair, the whole county'll be out. I haven't been to the Lion's Ball in over five years. Now, honestly, tell me, am I all right?

BECK Mai, you're a picture.

MILLIE You are, Mom.

GRANDMA F An apparition if ever I saw wan.

BECK Here, that'll start you off (*drink*).

THE MAI Pour one for Robert as well. He should be ready by now. And don't say anything about me looking well in front of him. See if he'll notice by himself and, Millie, would you get my cape, it's on the bed.

MILLIE *exits.* ROBERT *enters in a dress suit, his car keys dangling.*

ROBERT Right, are you ready?

THE MAI (*Hands him a drink*) This is poured for you.

ROBERT Thanks (*He and* THE MAI *drink*)

GRANDMA F Ya're looking very dashin', Robert.

ROBERT Am I?

He drinks, looks at THE MAI. THE MAI *looks at him.*

No compliment forthcoming. They finish the drinks.
MILLIE *enters with the cape and places it on* THE MAI'*s
shoulders.

Right, are we off? Goodnight.

He goes out.

THE MAI   (*Kisses* GRANDMA FRAOCHLÁN) Will you be OK?
GRANDMA F Will you?
THE MAI   I'm going to have a ball!

*With mock bravado she turns and smiles at them, and
goes out.* BECK *goes to the stereo and puts on Wagner's
'Liebestod' from* Tristan and Isolde, *turns down the
lights, pulls an opium pipe out of her shirt, shakes it at*
GRANDMA FRAOCHLÁN.

GRANDMA F (*Laughs*) A girl after me own heart.
BECK   (*Lights it up*) Here, you go first.

GRANDMA FRAOCHLÁN *takes four or five puffs, holds
them in, exhales slowly, smiles. As the conversation
goes on and the opium takes effect, it becomes apparent,
they're dreamy, slur some words, smile unexpectedly.*

GRANDMA F This must be whah it's like in Zanzibar.
BECK   (*Puffing*) What?
GRANDMA F Zanzibar. We'll go in an aeroplane through tha sky
           an' ax thim ta stop at Zanzibar.
BECK   Zanzibar, where's that?
GRANDMA F (*One arm out, then the other one*) It's way off thah way
           somewhere. Whah's ih like in an aeroplane, Beck?
BECK   Ever sat in a can of beans?
GRANDMA F (*Amazed*) Jaysus, we'll go be tha currach so. Whah
           d'ya think, Beck? Down th'Atlantic ocean, through
           tha straits a Gibraltar, an inta th'Arabian gulf, tha
           hills a Kilimanjira ta tha left, down be Mogadisha, a
           little more ta tha left or is ih tha righ', anaway there
           we are in Zanzibar! (*She puffs again,* BECK *lies back,*

relaxes) Tha nine-fingered fisherman an' meself used ta do this tha odd time.

BECK Yeah?

GRANDMA F I often wondert whah ih'd be like if he was still here, me nine-fingered fisherman, he'd be a hundert an' four.

BECK (*Laughs*) Would he?

GRANDMA F He would. Isn't tha worlt so strange, Beck?

BECK Always thought it more ordinary than strange.

GRANDMA F People, everywan is strange. I mane we're puh here wud natin' an' we'll lave wud natin' an' why does God in his heaven do thah t'us?

BECK I've been all over, and everywhere people are the same way. Everything's the same everywhere, they get up and go to work and come home and have their dinner and go to bed and make love or don't make love. And on the weekends they drive to the country if they're from the city and to the city if they're from the country. And some grow weary of that and just stay at home. (*Quite spaced*)

GRANDMA F I mane, does God want his childer ta suffer all tha time?

A pause. They both stare ahead, thinking.

(*On her own tangent*) Take my life now, I cem inta tha worlt withouh a father — born ta an absolute nuh. Was thah my fault? An' she wouldn't leh me call 'er Mother, no, Tha Duchess, thah's whah I had ta call her, or Duchess for short. An' Tha Duchess toult me me father was tha Sultan a Spain an' thah he'd hid Tha Duchess an' meself an Fraochlán because we were too beauhiful for tha worlt. Buh in tha summer he was goin' ta come in a yach' an' take us away ta his palace in Spain. An' we'd be dresst in silks an' pearls an' have Blackamoors dancin' attindence an us an' everywan an Fraochlán'd be cryin' wud jealousy — an' I believt her an' watched an tha cliffs ever'day for tha Sultan a Spain. An' ah th'end a every summer tha Sultan would noh've arrived an' ah th'end a every

59

summer Tha Duchess'd say, ih musta bin next summer he meant.

BECK (*In stitches*) Jesus, what a fruitcake!

GRANDMA F An' I don't know which of us believt thah story more — her nor me. I was tha on'y bastard an Fraochlán in livin' memory an' tha stigma must've bin terrible for her. I don't know, buh I'm noh over tha dismantlin' a thah drame yeh. Even still, every summer, I expect somethin' momentous ta happen. Whah's thah music anaway?

BECK (*Lost in her own thoughts*) Whah?

GRANDMA F An' thah's why whin Ellen goh pregnant, I would noh have tha scandal. I seen whah ih done ta Tha Duchess. Oh Ellen — She was heartbroken, Beck, ah where she'd arrived an' no one nor natin' could console her.

BECK I went to see him.

GRANDMA F Who? Whah?

BECK My father, passin' through London on my way home.

GRANDMA F Oh thah fella! (*Waves her hand dismissively*)

BECK A pleasant, mild-mannered man was what I met. I had tea with them. He's two teenage daughters. Put on a wonderful spread for me.

GRANDMA F (*Wearily*) I'm sure ih was all for show.

BECK Can you not leave the man his dignity and his new life, for fuck's sake! Why do you have to trample everything into the dirt! And he wasn't the illiterate boor you'd have us all believe. They went to great efforts to make me feel welcome though I'm sure I was the visit he'd been dreading for years. And do you know what he said to me? The last time I saw you, you were peerin' through the bars of the cot. And I almost answered, why didn't you lift me from that cot and take me away from that house of proud mad women!

GRANDMA F Did he ask for me?

BECK (*Snorts, turns to attack, sees* GRANDMA FRAOCHLÁN, *a frail, selfish old woman, and relents*) Sure. Sure he did.

GRANDMA F Beck, I was afraid whah everywan'd say, afraid they'd blem me an' say ih was Tha Duchess' blood as med her wild an' immoral.

THE MAI *stands in the doorway unnoticed.*

BECK Ah the past, the past, the past — Just forget it.

GRANDMA F Buh I shouldn't a cared. Ellen could a had The Mai an her own an' I could a minded her an' she could a gone an an' had tha very best a lives — a beauhiful stillborn baby boy, an' Ellen dead aside him — oh tha ligh' left my worlt an' I'll noh enter heaven withouh a spell below for whah I done ta thah girl.

THE MAI *moves into the room. She throws the car keys onto the table.* BECK *and* GRANDMA FRAOCHLÁN *jump with fright.* BECK *goes to hide the pipe.*

THE MAI Don't bother hidin' it. I've smelt it all over the house. It's an old familiar smell.

BECK We made sure the children were in bed, Mai, be-fore —

THE MAI Here, give me a puff and don't worry about the children. They know everything though they pretend not to. They want to protect me. (*She puffs on the pipe*)

BECK What're you doin' home so early?

GRANDMA F Puh ih (*the pipe*) away now so Robert doesn't see ih.

THE MAI Don't mind Robert. You could get used to this. (*Puffs*)

GRANDMA F Another figh'?

THE MAI Happy?

GRANDMA F I'm fed up a everywan blemin' me for everythin' around here. Sign meself inta a nursin' home if ye're noh careful!

THE MAI Yeah, another fight.

BECK Poor Cinderella. (*She bursts out laughing.* THE MAI *looks at her*) Sorry Mai, it's not me, it's the opium. (*She roars again*)

GRANDMA F Beck, behavin' ya'arself. (*Now she bursts out laughing*) Sorry, Mai. Sih down, whah happent?

THE MAI What happened? (*Laughs*) Here, give us another puff of that yoke.

BECK Where's Robert?

THE MAI   And ye had a great auld heartrendin' reminisce about
          your darlin' Ellen stranglin' herself in childbirth!

          ROBERT *appears in the doorway, sways, looks at them,
          points a finger vaguely, begins to speak, waves his
          hand, and makes for the drinks cabinet.*

          How did you get home? I suppose she ferried you!
ROBERT   Grandma Fraochlán, you'll join me? (*A drink*)
GRANDMA F I won't, Robert. Thank ya'anaway.
ROBERT   Mai? (*Offers decanter,* THE MAI *looks away*) So it's the
          silent treatment, is it? Well, that's to be expected.
          Sláinte. (*Drinks, toasts himself*) Sláinte, Robert. And
          did you have a good night, Robert? I've had better,
          but I'm sure The Mai has told you all about it.
THE MAI   You're drunk!
ROBERT   Wasn't a crime the last time I checked. What do you
          think, Grandma Fraochlán, of The Mai and me?
GRANDMA F Ya needn't be usin' me as a decoy. If ya've anathin' ta
          say ta Tha Mai, say ih ta her.
ROBERT   The Mai will not listen, because, you see, The Mai
          thinks in absolutes. And I am The Mai's absolute
          husband and when I refuse to behave as The Mai's
          absolute husband, The Mai shuts down because the
          reality of everyday living is too complicated for The
          Mai.
THE MAI   What reality are you speaking about, Robert?
ROBERT   Oh, you are listening.
THE MAI   What reality?
ROBERT   Love, the reality of love.
THE MAI   Thought you didn't believe in it.
ROBERT   And neither do I, but I believe in its absence, I believe
          in the black hole it leaves after it, like the way —
THE MAI   He left me in the middle of the floor to dance with
          her.
ROBERT   What's the big deal, if you hadn't created such a fuss!
          Ah but you love the auld bit of drama and fuss, don't
          you, Mai?
THE MAI   And I was calling you.
ROBERT   (*Mimics her*) Robert. Robert. You looked a right eejit!

62

THE MAI Why wouldn't you give me the car keys?

ROBERT You got them in the end, so what are you whinin' about!

THE MAI Why wouldn't you give them to me when I asked you the first time? He needed them to drive her home! That wagon with her sorry eyes. Even she was ashamed of you and I'd say it'd take a lot to shame her. And he's sittin' there with his arm around her! It was me you were taking out tonight. Me! And I literally begged him. I said, Robert, please don't leave me here on my own, begging for the car keys, and everyone was looking, and do you know what —

ROBERT Fuck the neighbours! Just look at you, my good wife. You're so fuckin' good, Mai, you even look good when we have a row in public.

THE MAI I just wanted the car keys so I could come home, you fucker!

ROBERT My beautiful wife with her beautiful body and her beautiful face and the goodness shining out of her. What am I supposed to do with all this beauty?

THE MAI And that weasel sittin' there, if I'd a knife I'd have put it through her!

ROBERT You'd do no such thing. You'll calm down as you always do and look me over with that hurt and patient expression that seems to be always on your face these days, at least when I am around, and I'll feel like the bastard I am.

THE MAI I want to know what she said about me!

As ROBERT *goes to exit* THE MAI *grabs him.*

I said I want to know what she —

ROBERT Let go of me. Look, she said nothing. I refuse to talk to her about you.

THE MAI But she talks about me, doesn't she? Oh yes she does, she talks about me in that arrogant way the loved one talks about the unloved!

ROBERT She does no such thing!

THE MAI (*Desperate*) She does, she does, she says something like, so you no longer love your wife, Robert? And

63

you say, I love my wife but I'm no longer in love with her or some bullshit like that. Isn't that the way it goes?

ROBERT No, it's not the way it goes, and I'm not discussing this any further with you!

THE MAI You won't discuss me with her and you discuss her with me. What will you discuss?

ROBERT I've told you a thousand times, my private life is my own business.

THE MAI Your private life! I am your private life! You invent these ridiculous compartments! You'll never be a great composer with —

ROBERT The last thing I need at this hour is a lecture from —

THE MAI You'll never be a great composer with such crude and vulgar compartments!

ROBERT I'm going to bed!

THE MAI That's right. Pretend none of this is happening. Go on to bed and dream of that ignorant fucking bitch!

ROBERT How dare you speak of her like that!

THE MAI How dare I? You may be in love with her but don't for one second think that I am, you shit!

ROBERT Will you for fuck's sake stop cursing. You sound like a fuckin' tinker!

THE MAI When you came back here after five years stravagin' up and down the world, you swore to me that you had changed —

ROBERT I said I would try to change. I promised nothing!

THE MAI You told me you loved me. If that's not a promise, what is? You told me you loved me and tonight you left me in the middle of the dance floor in front of everyone —

ROBERT Oh we're back to the neighbours, are we?

THE MAI Leave the neighbours out of this, I'm talking about —

ROBERT It was you brought them up!

THE MAI I'm talking about your treatment of me! Have you no decency left!

ROBERT The neighbours now are an interesting phenomonon, The Mai —

THE MAI That's right, skirt around everything, you fuckin' coward you.

ROBERT   The Mai is fascinated by the neighbours, all her —

THE MAI   You're a vicious fucking bastard without an ounce of —

ROBERT   All The Mai's efforts go into impressing the neighbours. She even goes so far as to insist she behave exactly like the neighbours on all occasions, but tonight, you see, we had a bit of a tiff and the neighbours hadn't, no, they conducted themselves with their usual dagger decorum, and what has The Mai upset now is —

THE MAI   You know absolutely nothing. You know fuck all about anything!

ROBERT   What has The Mai upset is not the fact that we had a row in public, but that the neighbours hadn't. If they had, then The Mai could've laughed off all the abuse I showered on her. I don't give a fuck about the neighbours and what upsets me, Mai, is that tonight I discovered I don't give a damn about you anymore!

GRANDMA F   Ya've said enough, Robert!

ROBERT   No, you keep out of this, Grandma Fraochlán. With all due respect you're just a visitor here!

THE MAI   It's you who's the visitor!

ROBERT   C'mon, Mai, you can do better than that!

THE MAI *wallops him across the face. He grabs her wrist.*

Get it through your thick little head that I am not one of your pupils!

GRANDMA F   Would ye stop!

THE MAI   (*Shaking her wrist free*) I'll have you know I came first in every exam I ever sat!

ROBERT   Degrees, degrees, you collect them like weapons!

THE MAI   And what do you have! Just your pissy little job at the college that my family got for you!

ROBERT   I got it myself this time!

THE MAI   And your pretensions to be a great composer and your mother whingein' in the background, oh, and you've your mistress, all great composers have to have a mistress!

ROBERT It's like tryin' to reason with a brick wall!

THE MAI And I was called up in front of the school board because of you, you bastard!

ROBERT Poor Mai, the whole town is on your back!

THE MAI And I stood up for you. And what about your children! Robert, you cannot treat people the way you are treating me. And that bitch, I went to see her you know and the way she —

ROBERT I heard all about it!

THE MAI And you say you don't talk about me! Of course you do! You fuckin' liar, on top of everything else!

ROBERT (*Turns on* GRANDMA FRAOCHLÁN *and* BECK) What are ye two doin' here! You can't turn round in this house without findin' one of the Connemara click behind you!

THE MAI (*Bursting into tears*) And you never collected me from the hospital when Stephen was born.

She falls to the floor, weeping.

ROBERT Ah now, Mai, come on, come on.

THE MAI No, go away from me!

ROBERT Mai, I tried, the car broke down, for Jesus' sake. What do you want from me, that was fourteen years ago.

THE MAI You think I can put up with anything, with the way you look at me these days, the way you despise me and trample over everything I have worked and fought so hard for. You think I can put up with anything, well I can't.

BECK C'mon, Mai, up.

ROBERT C'mon now. C'mon. (*To* BECK) It's OK. I'll put her to bed.

THE MAI No, leave me alone!

She gets up herself and exits. GRANDMA FRAOCHLÁN, BECK *and* ROBERT *look after her.* BECK *follows.*

BECK Mai.

GRANDMA FRAOCHLÁN *gets up and exits.* ROBERT, *left*

there, exits.

MILLIE *switches on the Christmas tree lights, and puts on a Christmas record.*

Next day.

THE MAI *enters with sunglasses on. She pours a drink for herself, sits by the window, apart from the others.* ROBERT *enters with a newspaper, sits down, looks at* THE MAI *when she's not looking. She does the same. Silence for a minute.* JULIE *enters with her handbag, followed by* AGNES *with hers, followed by* BECK *with a tea tray.*

JULIE That was a mighty spread, Mai.

THE MAI Beck did it all.

JULIE (*To* GRANDMA FRAOCHLÁN) Would you mind not blowin' that pipe up me nose!

GRANDMA F Sorry, sorry.

JULIE Gives me an awful headache.

AGNES And Julie has a very weak chest.

GRANDMA F Will I puh ih ouh? Thah whah ya're sayin'!

JULIE Ara I'll sit over beside Robert. What're you doin' readin' the paper on Christmas day! You're like my Michael, Lord rest him, he'd read the paper in the dark.

BECK I suppose ye went to the graveyard for Christmas.

AGNES Of course we did, looked in on the whole family, God rest them all. I love graveyards, so does Julie.

JULIE The graves were in an awful state after the winter. Michael has sunk another foot and his tombstone's cracked. I'll have to order another one.

AGNES It's the bog, keeps sinkin'.

JULIE Such a stupid place to have a graveyard. Maybe my Christmas present wasn't such a good idea after all, Agnes.

AGNES Julie bought me a plot beside her own for Christmas.

JULIE Well it's not exactly beside mine. It's the other side of Michael. It was the nearest I could get.

A snort from ROBERT, *behind the newspaper.*

67

GRANDMA F (*Half to herself*) Jaysus, poor Michael.

THE MAI It's beautiful there though, the way the tide comes in around it.

GRANDMA F Whin my time comes I'm ta be thrun inta tha wide Atlantic! D'ye all hear thah? Twinty mile sou'west a Fraochlán where tha nine-fingered fisherman's currach wint down! D'ye hear me now!

JULIE Ara, would ya stop such morbid talk on Christmas day.

ROBERT Well I'll be off. See ye all later. Ye're stopping a few days?

JULIE Tonight anyway.

ROBERT 'Bye everybody.

BECK 'Bye.

AGNES 'Bye Robert.

JULIE Where's he off to?

THE MAI Oh, visitin' his cronies, I suppose.

AGNES On Christmas day?

BECK Lots of people go visitin' on Christmas day.

JULIE Not in Connemara they don't, and not on their own. I wouldn't have that, Mai, he should be in playing with the children. That right, Agnes? (*Cute wink, returned by* AGNES)

THE MAI Ah — well —

AGNES You're too soft on him, Mai, isn't that it?

THE MAI Yeah, that's it.

GRANDMA F On Christmas day tha nine-fingered fisherman an' meself used ta go ta bed for th'afternoon wud a bottle a poitín an' a porter cake an' we'd sing all tha Christmas carols we knew.

JULIE It was some racket!

GRANDMA F A lovely way ta spind Christmas day. Did I ever tell ye as how he cem ta be calt tha nine-fingered fisherman?

JULIE About ten thousand times.

AGNES Ah, Julie, leave her, she's old.

JULIE Well, so am I.

GRANDMA F I won't open me mouh agin.

BECK Go on, you tell it every Christmas.

GRANDMA F I will noh indeed.

JULIE   Ara go on outa that, you're dyin' to tell it!

GRANDMA F   I am noh so.

BECK   Ah go on.

GRANDMA F   It was me third birth an' Tomás was ah sea. He didn't
             wanta go ouh an account a my impendin' delivery
             buh word cem tha salmon was leppin' an tha 'Bofin
             side. He'd bin ouh a day an' a nigh' whin he felt there
             was somethin' wrong of me. An' so there was,
             twinty-two hours gruntin', an' noh a sign a tha chilt's
             head. Tomás axed tha skipper ta turn round an' tha
             skipper refused an account a tha big haul, anaway tha
             nets was ouh. So in he jumped an' swam for
             Fraochlán, tha skipper follyin' him in tha boah,
             beggin' him ta get back an boord, fearin' he'd be
             drownt, every neh an Fraochlán in ribbons. Middle a
             tha nigh' ih was. I see him arrivin' in tha bed
             chamber drinched an' shiverin', his skin a livid
             purple from tha freezin' sea. He examines me an' sees
             I am alive an' thin he feel for tha pulse a tha new
             infant, Donal ih was. An' thin he collapses, doesn't
             come round for days. He lost tha little finger an his
             left hand an' from there an in he was known as tha
             nine-fingered fisherman. He wore thah missin'
             finger like a trophy for me. An' up an' down tha coast
             tha story becem known as how he'd lost ih. Boats
             would row up alongside his boah an' ax ta see his
             hand an' ax ta tell how he had come ta lose thah finger
             though tha'd heard tha story a hundert times already
             because people never tire a greah love stories.

JULIE   If it's true.

GRANDMA F   Ya're determint ta lave me wud natin'!

AGNES   Ah, of course it's true.

BECK   I'd love to have known him.

GRANDMA F   Sure ya would.

JULIE   I hardly remember him though. I was nearly thirteen
             when —

GRANDMA F   I know he was a useless father, Julie, I know, an' I was
             a useless mother. It's tha way we were med! There's
             two types a people in this worlt from whah I can
             gather, thim as puts their childer first an' thim as

69

puts their lover first an' for whah it's worth, tha nine-fingered fisherman an' meself belongs ta tha lahher a these. I would gladly a hurlt all seven a ye down tha slopes a hell for wan nigh' more wud tha nine-fingered fisherman an' may I roh eternally for such unmotherly feelin'.

BECK   I hear you're giving a flower arrangin' class, Agnes.

AGNES   Ah, it's only a little bit of a class at the Comprehensive.

GRANDMA F   Y'allas loved tha flowers, didn't ya, Agnes?

AGNES   I did. I did. Remember we used to go pickin' them up around the cliffs, yourself, myself and Ellen, up by Sruthán na mBláth.

THE MAI   The river of flowers. I remember Mom talking about it. Once, I said to her, wouldn't you love to be somewhere else, Mom? Yes, she said. Where would you like to be? I'd like to be a child again, she said, up to my knees in Sruthán na mBláth, underneath me the golden sand. I'd like to walk up that river forever.

AGNES   Ellen was an awful dreamer.

JULIE   A gangly unbiddable girl with her two feet planted firmly in the clouds.

AGNES   She was beautiful and wild before she met your father.

JULIE   Wild, don't be talkin'!

THE MAI *goes out.*

AGNES   The pair of us were at every dogfight in Connemara lookin' for men and they all fell for Ellen.

BECK   I'm sure a few fell for you too.

AGNES   Not at all, I was always on the plain side.

GRANDMA F   Ya never were, who toult ya thah?

AGNES   You did.

GRANDMA F   I never did, must be thinkin' a somewan else, *a chroí.*

JULIE   What's up with The Mai?

BECK   Ah she's probably tired.

MILLIE   None of The Mai and Robert's children are very strong. We teeter along the fringe of the world with halting gait, reeking of Owl Lake at every turn. I dream of water all the time. I'm floundering off the shore, or bursting towards the surface for air, or wrestling with a black swan trying to drag me under. I have not yet emerged triumphant from those lakes of the night. Sometimes I think I wear Owl Lake like a caul around my chest to protect me from all that is good and hopeful and worth pursuing. And on a confident day when I am considering a first shaky step towards something within my grasp, the caul constricts and I am back at Owl Lake again. Images rush past me from that childhood landscape. There's The Mai talking to the builders about the dimensions of Robert's study and there's Robert playing football with Stephen and Jack, and Orla on her swing. Now Grandma Fraochlán is lighting her pipe as Beck wanders in and pours a drink. There's The Mai again, adding up the bills, a pencil in her mouth, Robert making his cello sing, The Mai at the window, Grandma Fraochlán's oar, Julie and Agnes collude-rin' in the corner, The Mai at the window and The Mai at the window again, and it goes on and on till I succumb and linger among them there in that dead silent world that tore our hearts out for a song.

> THE MAI *enters in a nightdress — it is the middle of the night — she goes to the stereo and puts on some cello music, then goes to the window, and stares out.*

Mom?

THE MAI Ah Millie, I couldn't sleep. Go on back to bed.

MILLIE Robert not home yet?

THE MAI No.

MILLIE Why don't you leave him?

THE MAI Millie, please.

MILLIE Or ask him to leave. Or have an affair.

THE MAI I already did.

MILLIE You did not.

THE MAI A one-night stand, to be more precise, a one-night stand with a stranger passing through — I shouldn't be telling you all this — I know now why Robert does it, it's the excitement, the newness, it's powerful and it's wonderful, not old and weak like an eighteen year marriage. You'll be different, won't you, Millie? You won't be like me and Robert — Maybe he still loves me. What do you think, Millie?

MILLIE Mom, I don't know.

THE MAI No, Millie, he does, he loves me in his own high damaged way. Maybe it's just a phase he's going through and in a few years he'll come back to me — What do you think, Millie?

MILLIE I don't know.

THE MAI Millie, I don't think anyone will ever understand, not you, not my family, not even Robert, no one will ever understand how completely and utterly Robert is mine and I am his, no one — People think I've no pride, no dignity, to stay in a situation like this, but I can't think of one reason for going on without him.

MILLIE Mom, you've never tried.

THE MAI I don't want to.

MILLIE Come on back to bed, you can sleep in beside me.

THE MAI You go on, you're tired.

MILLIE You'll come shortly?

THE MAI Yeah.

MILLIE *watches* THE MAI *looking out the window. A few seconds later,* THE MAI *turns and drifts from the room. Sounds of geese and swans taking flight, sounds of water. Silence.*
Lights down.